CHEMISTRY

GCSE Grade Booster

P. A. Fryer

Schofield & Sims Ltd.

0 7217 4614 4

First printed 1989

Schofield & Sims Ltd.
Dogley Mill
Fenay Bridge
Huddersfield
HD8 0NQ
England

Designed by Ocean Typesetting, Leeds
Printed in England by Alden Press

Contents

Introduction 4
1 Mixtures and Compounds 5
2 Solids, Liquids and Gases 10
3 Composition of Matter 13
4 Atomic Structure 15
5 Formulae and Equations 24
6 Counting Atoms and Molecules 27
7 Electrochemistry 32
8 Acids, Bases and Salts 37
9 Oxidation and Reduction 44
10 Air 48
11 Water 50
12 Oxygen and Hydrogen 53
13 Periodic Table 56
14 Metals 59
15 Salt to Chlorine 66
16 Limestone and Carbon Dioxide 69
17 Rates of Reaction 73
18 Sulphur and Nitrogen 76
19 Carbon 82
20 Energy and Chemical Change 89
21 Tests for Common Substances and Ions 93
Index 96

Introduction

This Chemistry Grade Booster is written to help you revise in the last part of your GCSE course. It is not intended as a textbook and you should use a text and/or your notes to check details. You should also read your syllabus to see if there are any sections you can omit.

The book is arranged in such a way that it will be convenient for revision. Throughout you will find headings and subheadings in the margin, with definitions, explanations, equations, examples, etc., to the right of the margin. Use a card with the book to expose the keyword in the margin, but keep the right-hand side covered. Then try to recall the material on the right. By careful lowering of the card, you can allow yourself to see just enough of the writing to prompt you.

Remember that there are several aspects of the GCSE Chemistry course not covered or only touched on in a book like this. One such aspect is laboratory work on which you will be assessed, but which is still likely to appear in written exam papers. You need to study your practical note book and experiment sheets.

Acknowledgements

The author would like to thank colleagues at Bradford and Ilkley Community College for their encouragement, reviewers in schools who made many helpful comments, and in particular Mrs. Halina Reid for accurately typing a daunting hand-written final draft.

Thanks are also due in no small measure to the author's wife and family for their tolerance and support during the writing period.

P. A. Fryer

1 Mixtures and Compounds

Chemistry   Chemistry is the science concerned with the properties of different kinds of matter and the way in which one kind of matter reacts with another kind.

States of Matter   There are three states of matter:

solid (s),

liquid (l),

gas (g).

The symbol in brackets is referred to as the state symbol.

The symbol (aq) is the symbol used to refer to *aqueous* (water) *solutions*.

Mixtures   Mixtures are made of more than one pure substance.

Pure Substances   Pure substances may be elements existing on their own or may be compounds.

Elements   Elements are pure substances that contain only one kind of atom.

Compounds   Compounds are pure substances containing more than one element. They have their own properties which are characteristic for the compound.

Differences between Mixtures and Compounds

	Mixture	Compound
Composition	Composition can be variable (i.e. any amount of each component).	Composition is fixed (i.e. the elements are present in a fixed ratio).
Properties	The properties are those possessed by each of the components.	The properties are characteristic for the particular compound.
Separation	Separation into the component pure substances *can* be achieved by physical means (i.e. not by a chemical reaction).	Separation into component elements *can not* be achieved by physical means.

5

Example	Mixture: iron powder and sulphur powder	Compound: iron (II) sulphide
Composition	—	Iron and sulphur atoms present in a constant ratio of 1:1. (Formula: FeS).
Properties	1. The mixture has appearance of grey with yellow specks (iron, powder-grey; sulphur, powder-yellow).	1. The compound is dark grey/black solid in appearance.

	2. The mixture reacts with dilute hydrochloric acid to evolve a gas which explodes when ignited in air,*
	i.e. iron + hydrochloric acid
	→hydrogen + iron (II) chloride
	
	or $Fe(s) + 2HCl(aq)$
	   $→H_2(g) + FeCl_2(aq)$
	*Pure iron powder has the same reaction.
		2. The compound reacts with dilute hydrochloric acid to give off a gas with a smell of rotten eggs,
		
		i.e. iron (II) sulphide +
		    hydrochloric acid
		→hydrogen sulphide +
		    iron (II) chloride
		or $FeS(s) + 2HCl(aq)$
		   $→H_2S(g) + FeCl_2(aq)$

	3. When ignited, burns with a blue flame giving off a gas with a choking smell,* i.e. sulphur + oxygen →sulphur dioxide or $S(s) + O_2(g)→SO_2(g)$ *Pure sulphur burns in the same way.	3. Iron (II) sulphide does not burn.
Separation	A magnet will separate the iron from the mixture.	

Note: When the mixture of iron and sulphur powder is heated, a highly *exothermic* (see page 89) reaction occurs and iron (II) sulphide is formed.

iron + sulphur → iron (II) sulphide
$Fe(s) + S(s)$ $→ FeS(s)$

This is a chemical change.

Separation of Mixtures In order to separate mixtures, we need to employ differences in the physical properties of the components.

Differences These may be differences of, for instance, solubility or boiling point.

Experimental Techniques We rely on various experimental techniques.

Dissolution Dissolution is dissolving a substance, the *solute* (see page 11), in a solvent.

Filtration Filtration is adding a mixture of a solid and liquid to a filter paper folded into a filter funnel. The solid remains in the paper as a residue while the liquid passes through as the filtrate.

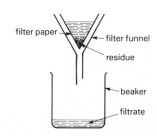

Centrifugation Centrifugation is a mechanical means of separating a solid and a liquid by spinning the mixture in a centrifuge at high speed so that the heavier solid is thrown to the bottom. The liquid above the solid is then poured or sucked off.

Distillation Distillation is the technique where a liquid mixture is boiled so that the components vaporise and condense in order of increasing boiling point (i.e. the liquid with the lowest boiling point boils first).

Simple distillation

7

Fractional distillation This is as for distillation, but the apparatus includes a 'fractionating' column between the distillation flask and the condenser.

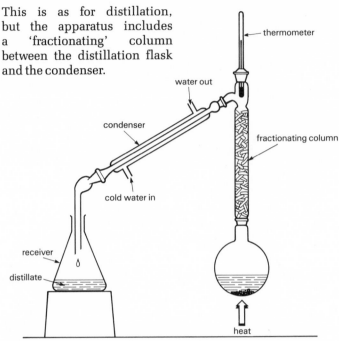

Fractional distillation

Evaporation Evaporation is boiling a liquid mixture of a solid dissolved in a solvent to evaporate the unwanted solvent and leave the solid.

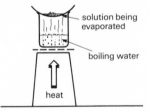

Chromatography In chromatography, a spot of the liquid mixture is placed near the bottom of paper, which is then dipped in a solvent below the spot. The components in the mixture rise up the paper at different rates and are separated as coloured spots.

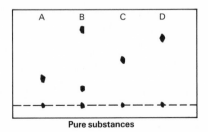

Pure substances

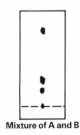

Mixture of A and B

Types of Separation	
Solid from a liquid in which it is insoluble	Consider sand and water.
	The technique used is *filtration*. (The residue must be washed).
Solid from its solution in an unwanted solvent	Consider salt in water.
	The technique used is *evaporation*. (Care must be taken not to heat the remaining solid too much in case it decomposes.) This can safely be achieved using a water bath.
Two liquids which are mixed	Consider water and alcohol.
	The technique used is *distillation*, based on the differing boiling points of the two liquids.
	When the boiling points are close together, or when the mixture is more complicated, then *fractional distillation* is used. The condensed liquids obtained at different stages are called *fractions*.
Coloured substances in dyes	Consider dyes; also, food colouring.
	The technique used is *chromatography*.
Two solids which are dissolved in the same solvent	Consider potassium nitrate and potassium chloride in water.
	The technique used is *crystallisation*, based on the different solubilities of the solids (see page 11).
Two solids, one of which sublimes on heating	Consider salt and iodine.
	The technique is to *heat and allow the vapour of one of the solids to settle on a cool surface*. The iodine sublimes. (*Sublimation* is the process whereby, on heating, a solid is converted directly from solid to vapour, i.e. it does not melt to a liquid.)
Industrial Separation	
Air	Air is first liquefied, then fractional distillation is used. Nitrogen boils first at −196°C, before oxygen at −183°C. (Remember that −196°C is a lower temperature than −183°C.)
Petroleum	The components of petroleum (crude oil) are treated in an oil refinery, initially by fractional distillation. See Chapter 19 (page 84) on the 'fractions' collected.

2 Solids, Liquids and Gases

Changes of State

$$SOLID \underset{\text{freezing}}{\overset{\text{melting}}{\rightleftharpoons}} LIQUID \underset{\text{condensation}}{\overset{\text{boiling or evaporation}}{\rightleftharpoons}} GAS$$

Melting point

Melting point (m.p.) is the temperature at which a solid melts to a liquid. A pure substance all melts at one constant temperature. Freezing point (f.p.) refers to the change from liquid to solid.

Boiling point

Boiling point (b.p.) is the constant temperature at which a pure liquid boils.

> Note: Boiling point is dependent on atmospheric pressure: lower pressure (e.g. up a mountain) → lower b.p.; higher pressure (e.g. pressure cooker) → higher b.p.

M.p. of impure solid

The m.p. of an impure solid is *lower* than that of pure substances (e.g. when salt is added to ice on roads).

B.p. of impure liquid

The b.p. of an impure liquid is *higher* than that of pure solvent.

Time-Temperature Graphs

If steady heat is applied to a solid and the temperature is recorded, a graph like this is obtained. Examine the graph and decide what is happening at each stage.

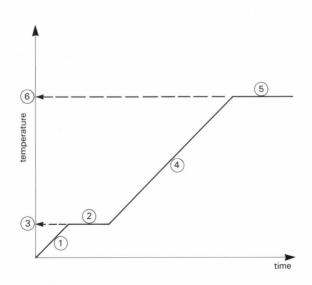

Stage 1	The solid absorbs heat on being warmed.
Stage 2	The solid uses absorbed heat to melt at a constant temperature.
Stage 3	Melting point.
Stage 4	The liquid absorbs heat as its temperature rises.
Stage 5	The liquid uses absorbed heat to boil at a constant temperature.
Stage 6	Boiling point.

Solutions and Solubility

Solute	The solute is the substance (solid, liquid or gas) dissolving in a solvent.
Solvent	The solvent is the liquid in which a solute dissolves to give a solution.
Solution	The solution is the mixture obtained.
Example	Salt (solute) in water (solvent) → salt solution.
Common solvents	Water, petrol, perchloroethene (used in dry-cleaning), alcohol, ether.
Saturated solution	A saturated solution is one in which as much solute is dissolved as possible at a particular temperature.
Solubility	Solubility is a measure of the amount of solute which can dissolve in a solvent. It is defined as: *the number of grams of solute which dissolve in 100 grams of the solvent at a particular temperature to give a saturated solution*.
Solubility of solids	Generally, the solubility of a solid increases as the temperature increases, but it is not linear (i.e. solubility does *not* double when temperature doubles).
Solubility of gases	Gases dissolve in liquids.
Example 1	Oxygen (in air) dissolves in water enabling plant and animal life in rivers and lakes to survive.
Example 2	Carbon dioxide dissolves in rain water giving an acidic solution, which may fall on limestone rocks, giving a type of hard water.
Effect of temperature	As the temperature increases, less gas dissolves.
Effect of pressure	If the pressure is increased, more gas will dissolve in a liquid, i.e. fizzy drinks.
Solubility Curve	A solubility curve is a graph of solubility of a solute (vertical axis) against temperature.

You may have performed an experiment to obtain a solubility curve like the following:

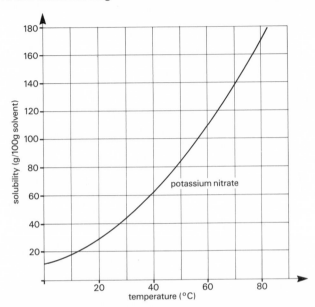

Remember that in an experimental graph the points do not always lie exactly on a smooth curve or straight line.

Uses of
Solubility

1. Determining the solubility at an unknown temperature.

    For instance, what is the solubility of potassium nitrate at 55°C?

    To find the answer, you would draw a vertical line at 55°C. At the point this meets the curve, you would draw a horizontal line to the solubility axis and read off the answer in g/100 g solvent. The answer is 96 g/100 g.

2. Separating substances dissolved in the same solvent by the method known as crystallisation.

3. Determining what mass of a solute will crystallise when a solution cools.

    For instance, suppose 150 g of potassium nitrate is dissolved in 100 g of water at 80°C. How much solid will crystallise if the solution is cooled to 20°C?

    Firstly, to find the answer, will all the 150 g dissolve at 80°C? Yes – from the graph, solubility at 80°C is 170 g. Secondly, how much will dissolve at 20°C? From the graph, 30g. Therefore 120 g (i.e. 150 – 30) will crystallise.

3 Composition of Matter

Evidence for Existence of Individual Particles

Diffusion Diffusion is the gradual mixing of one substance with another.

Examples of gas diffusion

1. The steam from a boiling kettle spreads throughout a room.
2. A gas jar of clear air on top of a gas jar of brown bromine (heavier than air) slowly mixes to form a lighter brown gas mixture.
3. A long tube with source of hydrogen chloride gas at one end and ammonia at the other slowly produces a white cloud at the end nearer the hydrogen chloride source. Why?

Because the ammonia is lighter (M_r = 17) than hydrogen chloride (M_r = 36.5) and so diffuses faster.

Examples of liquid diffusion

1. A dark crystal of potassium manganate (VII) added to a beaker of water slowly dissolves to give a purple solution.
2. The purple solution of potassium manganate (VII), when diluted with an equal amount of water, is still purple (but lighter); and with continued dilution, the purple colour (potassium manganate (VII) particles) can still be seen. The particles are spreading throughout the solution.

Kinetic Particle Theory The evidence above indicates that individual particles of a substance exist. How do the particles move and how are they different in gases, liquids and solids?

Particle movement is due to the possession of kinetic energy (the more energy they possess, the faster they move).

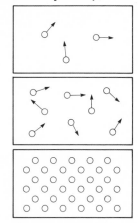

Gas Gas particles move fastest and move to fill whatever space is available.

Liquid Liquid particles move more slowly and are confined to the limits of the vessel in which they are put.

Solid Solid particles only possess sufficient energy to vibrate while held in a regular arrangement.

Liquid → Gas   On heating, a liquid absorbs heat energy which is converted to kinetic energy and particles move more quickly.

Compressi-bility of gases   When compressed, gas particles are forced into a smaller space and may be converted to a liquid (i.e. particles will be closer together).

Example   Gas cylinders – butane (liquefied gas fuel). Because of the high pressure, especially strong containers are needed.

> Note: Liquids and solids are hardly affected by compression.

Pressure, Volume and Temperature

P and *V* (at constant *T*)   As gas pressure increases, its volume decreases.

Example   Gas cylinders.

T and *V* (at constant *P*)   As the temperature of a gas increases its volume increases.

Example   A gas-filled balloon expanding in a warm room.

P and *T* (at constant *V*)   As the pressure on a gas increases, its temperature increases.

Example   In a bicycle pump.

4 Atomic Structure

Pure Substances	The individual particles referred to (in Chapter 3) are those of pure substances. Pure substances can be broken down into even smaller particles called *atoms*. These atoms usually are quite different in properties from the original substance.
Atoms	Atoms are the smallest particles of individual elements and have their own properties.
Elements	Elements of about 100 different types of atom exist. Of these 100 types, about 90 occur naturally; the other 10 or so are made by scientists in a laboratory or reactor. Each element is given a name and a symbol.
Chemical Symbol	A chemical symbol comprises one capital letter, or one capital followed by a small letter.

Examples

Name of element	Symbol for element
hydrogen	H
chlorine	Cl
iron	Fe
nitrogen	N
sodium	Na
zinc	Zn

> Note: You will probably have to be familiar with only about 30 elements and may have a data book to refer to. Check up on this.

Atoms and Molecules

Existence	Atoms of many elements cannot exist on their own and have to combine with other atoms of either the same element or other elements to form molecules.
Molecules	Molecules are defined as a group of atoms which are *bonded* (joined) together and which can exist as separate units.
Example	Hydrogen (H) atoms cannot exist as single atoms but two hydrogen atoms bond to form the hydrogen molecule, H_2. Hydrogen bonds with different atoms to form molecules such as water, H_2O.
Ions	Ions are atoms or molecules which undergo a change and exist as charged particles.

**Structure of
the Atom**

small
heavy
centre   surrounded by very light particles

Nucleus The nucleus is the small heavy centre of the atom, and consists of one or more protons and (except in the case of the smallest atom of hydrogen) one or more neutrons.

Protons Protons have a mass of about 1 unit, and have a $+1$ positive charge on each.

Neutrons Neutrons have about the same mass as protons and are neutral.

Electrons Electrons move very fast around the nucleus, are very light (about 1/2000 unit), and have a -1 negative charge on each.

**Atomic
Number or
Proton
Number (Z)** The atomic number (Z) is a number characteristic of a particular element, that represents the number of protons in the nucleus of an atom of that element.

Example 1 All hydrogen atoms contain 1 proton, so the atomic number of hydrogen is 1 (Z = 1).

Example 2 All chlorine atoms contain 17 protons, so the atomic number is 17 (Z = 17).

**Mass Number
or Nucleon
Number (A)** The mass number (A) is the sum of protons and neutrons in the nucleus of an atom. This can vary for an element.

Isotopes Isotopes are atoms of the same element (same atomic number and same number of protons) but with different numbers of neutrons (different mass number).

Example Chlorine (Z = 17) has two isotopes:
Cl (A = 35) – containing 17 protons and 18 neutrons, and
Cl (A = 37) – containing 17 protons and 20 neutrons.

**Chemical
similarity** Because isotopes have the same number of protons and electrons, isotopes of an element are chemically similar.

Nuclides Nuclides are the nuclei of specified isotopes and are written as, for instance, $^{37}_{17}Cl$.

$$A \rightarrow 37 \atop Z \rightarrow 17} Cl$$

**Isotopes in
everyday life** Many isotopes occur naturally and are present in the normal chemicals we use frequently:

chlorine – $^{35}_{17}Cl$ and $^{37}_{17}Cl$
copper – $^{63}_{29}Cu$ and $^{65}_{29}Cu$
hydrogen – $^{1}_{1}H$ (hydrogen), $^{2}_{1}H$ (deuterium) and $^{3}_{1}H$ (tritium).

Some isotopes are radioactive and emit harmful radiation.

Uses of isotopes   Isotopes are used for the benefit of mankind:
in medicine,
in archaeology,
in creating nuclear energy,
but, of course, can also be used for destructive purposes.

Radioactive

Relative Atomic Mass (A_r)   Relative atomic mass (A_r) is a measure of the mass of the 'average' atom of an element (taking into account the masses of the various isotopes present) on a scale which uses the carbon-12 isotopes as its base.

Example   Chlorine-35, present as 75% of Cl atoms.
Chlorine-37, present as 25% of Cl atoms.

Average mass (A_r) = (75% of 35) + (25% of 37) = 35.5
(Most values of A_r are approximated to whole numbers for GCSE use).

Relative Formula Mass (M_r)   Relative formula mass (M_r) is a measure of the mass of the average 'molecule' of a compound on the same scale as A_r. It is obtained by adding up the values of A_r for the different elements, taking into account the numbers of atoms of each element in the formula.

Example 1 H_2O
$A_r(H) = 1, \quad A_r(O) = 16$
$$M_r(H_2O) = \underset{H}{1} + \underset{H}{1} + \underset{O}{16}$$
$$= 18$$

Example 2 $(NH_4)_2CO_3$
$A_r(N) = 14, \quad A_r(H) = 1, \quad A_r(C) = 12, \quad A_r(O) = 16$
$$M_r[(NH_4)_2CO_3] = 2 \times (\underset{N}{14} + \underset{H}{1} + \underset{H}{1} + \underset{H}{1} + \underset{H}{1}) + \underset{C}{12} + \underset{O}{16} + \underset{O}{16} + \underset{O}{16}$$
$$= 96$$

Example 3 $CuSO_4.5H_2O$
(In examples where there is water of crystallisation the M_r for $5H_2O$ must be added to M_r for $CuSO_4$.)
$A_r(Cu) = 64, \quad A_r(S) = 32, \quad A_r(O) = 16, \quad M_r(H_2O) = 18$
$$M_r(CuSO_4.5H_2O) = \underset{Cu}{64} + \underset{S}{32} + \underset{O}{16} + \underset{O}{16} + \underset{O}{16} + \underset{O}{16} + (5 \times \underset{H_2O}{18})$$
$$= 250$$

Arrangement of Electrons

Energy Levels

Electrons exist at a distance from the nucleus, dependent on the amount of energy they possess (the more energy, the further away). Electrons can possess only certain amounts of energy, so that energy levels exist at which electrons can be found. At each level there is a maximum possible number of electrons.

Maximum Number of Electrons	nucleus $\oplus$	K shell (1st energy level)	L shell (2nd energy level)	M shell (3rd energy level)	N shell (4th energy level)
		2 electrons MAXIMUM	8 electrons MAXIMUM	8 electrons MAXIMUM*	

$$\longrightarrow$$
increasing energy

*This maximum is revised in more advanced courses.

Filling Energy Levels

Electrons will always be at the lowest level possible until the maximum number of electrons is present.

Example 1

Oxygen (Z = 8).
Since the atom is neutral, there will be 8 electrons as well as 8 protons.

level	K	L
electrons	2 (full)	6

(2 + 6 = 8)

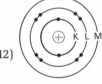

Example 2

Magnesium (Z = 12).

level	K	L	M
electrons	2 (full)	8 (full)	2

(2 + 8 + 2 = 12)

Example 3

Neon (Z = 10).

level	K	L
electrons	2 (full)	8 (full)

(2 + 8 = 10)

Bonding of Atoms

Noble gases

Electron arrangements for some of these unreactive elements are as follows.

	K	L	M	N	
He	2				
Ne	2	8			} all full levels
Ar	2	8	8		

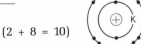

Reactive metals		K	L	M	N	
	Na	2	8	1		} 1 electron in
	K	2	8	8	1	outermost level

Reactive non-metals		K	L	M	N	
	F	2	7			} 1 electron less
	Cl	2	8	7		than full in outermost level

Reason for bonding Atoms bond with each other to form compounds in order to become more stable (less reactive). They do this by getting an electron arrangement like that of a noble gas (above), by gaining, losing or sharing electrons (e^-).

Electron Transfer Na atom 2, 8, 1 (1 e^- too many)

Cl atom 2, 8, 7 (1 e^- too few)

Sodium gives its outer electron to chlorine:

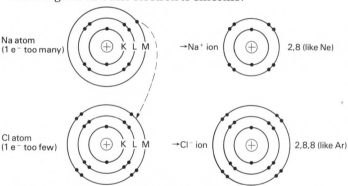

Na atom (1 e^- too many) → Na^+ ion 2,8 (like Ne)

Cl atom (1 e^- too few) → Cl^- ion 2,8,8 (like Ar)

Ions The Na^+ ion now has 11 protons (+)
but 10 electrons (−),

i.e. 1 more proton than electrons (hence +ve charge on ion).

The Cl^- ion now has 17 protons (+)
but 18 electrons (−),

i.e. 1 more electron than protons (hence −ve charge on ion).

Ionic bonding The Na^+ and the Cl^- ion are then attracted (opposite charges attract) to form sodium chloride:

$$Na^+ + Cl^- \rightarrow NaCl$$
sodium chloride

in which the ions are held together by an ionic bond.

Note: The new compound formed by ionic bonding has quite different properties from the component elements.

Magnesium Chloride If magnesium reacts with chlorine:

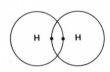

$$Mg \quad 2, \quad 8, \quad 2$$

Cl 2, 8, 7

1e⁻

but needs another Cl atom
to take the other electron

1e⁻   Cl 2, 8, 7

So Mg loses $2e^- \longrightarrow Mg^{2+}$ 12 protons (+)
                                                 10 electrons (–)

2 Cl each gain $1e^- \longrightarrow 2Cl^-$

The compound formed is written as $MgCl_2$.

Electron Sharing When electrons are *shared* between two atoms, a covalent bond is formed.

Example 1 Hydrogen.
2 hydrogen atoms share 2 electrons to form H_2.

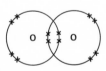

Each atom "thinks" it has $2e^-$ and so has the e^- arrangement of He.
The bond is represented thus:

H — H

Example 2 Oxygen.
2 oxygen atoms share 4 electrons (2 from each) to form O_2.

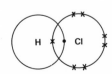

Each atom now has 8 electrons in outer level (6 of its own and 2 belonging to other atom).
The bond is represented thus:
O = O

Note: In 'dot-cross' diagrams like these, only the outermost energy levels are drawn.

Example 3 Hydrogen chloride.

. . . forming HCl, hydrogen chloride
The bond is represented thus:
H — Cl

Example 4   *Water.*

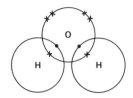

... forming H_2O, water
The bonding is represented:
$H - O - H$

Example 5   *Ammonia.*

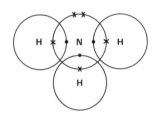

... forming NH_3, ammonia
The bonding is represented:

Example 6   *Methane.*

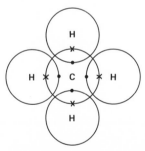

... forming CH_4, methane
The bonding is represented:

Bonding in Metals   Metals are composed of atoms with a small number of electrons in the outer energy level (e.g. sodium, magnesium). In the solid state these electrons are released to move throughout the metal structure, rather like a cloud or sea of electrons. These electrons form a kind of 'glue' holding the atoms together.

This is called metallic bonding.

Bond Type and Properties   The properties of a compound depend on the bonds between atoms and the bonds holding molecules to each other.

Simple molecules   *Hydrogen.*
$H - H$; strong covalent bonds between atoms. Weak bonds between H_2 molecules. Hydrogen is therefore a gas at room temperature.

21

Water.
H_2O; strong covalent bonds between H and O. Fairly strong bonds between water molecules, so they are more difficult to separate – water is a liquid at room temperature.

Paraffin Wax.
Strong covalent bonds between atoms. Bonds between the molecules are strong enough to make paraffin wax a solid at room temperature.

Giant molecular (or macro-molecular) solids

Some solids occur with covalent bonds which are not restricted to a few atoms in a molecule but are spread throughout a large structure. These are called giant molecular (or macro-molecular) solids.

Diamond.
A very hard substance with a high melting point. *Each* carbon atom is at the centre of a tetrahedron surrounded by four other carbon atoms.

All covalent bonds are the same strength. The hardness of diamond makes it useful to tip drill bits. It is a non-conductor of electricity.

Graphite.
Carbon atoms arranged in layers. The bonds in the layers are strong, but those holding the layers together are weak, so the layers can slide over one another.

Graphite conducts electricity (due to free electrons moving between layers). Its softness makes it useful in pencil 'leads'.

Sand.
SiO_2 – has a structure similar to that of diamond.

Poly(ethene).
A very large molecule made up of carbon and hydrogen.

Ionic solids

Ionic solids are arranged regularly in a pattern or lattice so that the maximum attraction of opposite ions is obtained, as for instance with sodium chloride.

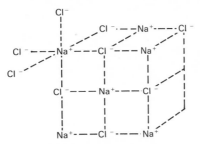

Each Na$^+$ is surrounded by 6 Cl$^-$ and each Cl$^-$ is surrounded by 6 Na$^+$.

Ionic solids have fairly high melting points (sodium chloride melts at 801°C) since the strong attractive forces between the ions have to be overcome in order to separate them to form a liquid.

Differences in Property between Ionic and Covalent Compounds

	Ionic compounds	Covalent compounds
Melting point	fairly high	generally low (except for giant covalent compounds)
Boiling point	fairly high	—
Solubility in water	generally soluble	generally insoluble
Solubility in organic solvents	insoluble	generally soluble
Electrical conductivity	solid state – no conductivity; molten state – good conductor; aqueous soln – good conductors	do not conduct (the exception is graphite)

5 Formulae and Equations

Ionic Compounds
The formulae for ions you have met up to now (e.g. Na^+, Mg^{2+}, Cl^-) are for simple ions composed of one element only. Other simple ions are:

Positive ions				Negative ions	
hydrogen	H^+	iron (II)	Fe^{2+}	bromide	Br^-
potassium	K^+	lead (II)	Pb^{2+}	fluoride	F^-
silver	Ag^+	zinc	Zn^{2+}	iodide	I^-
calcium	Ca^{2+}	aluminium	Al^{3+}	oxide	O^{2-}
copper (II)	Cu^{2+}	iron (III)	Fe^{3+}	sulphide	S^{2-}

More complex ions are also common. These consist of atoms of more than one element bonded together, but with a charge on the whole ion.

Positive ion		Negative ions			
ammonium	NH_4^+	hydroxide	OH^-	carbonate	CO_3^{2-}
		nitrate	NO_3^-	sulphate	SO_4^{2-}
		hydrogen-carbonate	HCO_3^-	sulphite	SO_3^{2-}
		hydrogen-sulphate	HSO_4^-		

> Note: Depending on your syllabus, you may be allowed to refer to a data book containing the formulae of these ions *or* you may have to learn them. Make sure you know which.

Writing Ionic Formulae
A correct ionic formula shows the number of positive and negative ions necessary to 'balance' the electrons donated by the positive ion and accepted by the negative ion, i.e. balance the charges.

Example 1
Sodium oxide (Na^+ with O^{2-}).
Two Na^+ needed (total 2^+) to balance one O^{2-} (total 2^-).

$$\therefore \text{formula} = Na_2O$$

The balancing 2 needs to be written as a subscript after the Na.

Example 2
Aluminium sulphide (Al^{3+} with S^{2-}).
Two Al^{3+} needed (total 6^+) to balance three S^{2-} (total 6^-).

$$\therefore \text{formula} = Al_2S_3$$

> Note: When complex ions are involved, you must remember to put the whole ion in brackets *if more than one of it is needed*, with the subscript outside the bracket.

Example 3 *Calcium nitrate* (Ca^{2+} with NO_3^-).

One Ca^{2+} needed (total 2^+) to balance two NO_3^- (total 2^-).

∴ formula = $Ca(NO_3)_2$

Example 4 *Ammonium sulphate* (NH_4^+ with SO_4^{2-}).

Two NH_4^+ needed (total 2^+) to balance one SO_4^{2-} (total 2^-).
∴ formula = $(NH_4)_2SO_4$

Example 5 *Potassium hydroxide* (K^+ with OH^-).

One K^+ needed (total 1^+) to balance one OH^- (total 1^-).

∴ formula = KOH (no brackets needed)

> Note:
> 1. The positive ion is always written first.
> 2. Never write the balancing numbers anywhere other than to the lower right of the ion.

Covalent Compounds   The number of electrons to be shared by an atom is often called its valency. In a similar way to ionic compounds, the total number of electrons shared by each atom must balance.

Example 1 *Water* [H(valency = 1) with O(valency = 2)].

∴ formula = H_2O

Example 2 *Ammonia* [N(valency = 3) with H(valency = 1)].

∴ formula = NH_3

Chemical Equations

What is a chemical equation?   A chemical equation is a shorthand representation of what happens in a chemical change. It shows which chemicals are involved and, in a symbol equation, the ratio of the numbers of molecules (see Chapter 6) of reactants to products.

Reactants   Reactants are the chemicals started with.

Products   Products are the chemicals formed.

REACTANTS $\longrightarrow$ PRODUCTS
give on reaction

Word equation   e.g. iron + sulphur → iron (II) sulphide

Symbol Equation $Fe(s)$ + $S(s)$ → $FeS(s)$

Law of conservation of mass	The law of conservation of mass is a basic law of nature which means that you finish a chemical reaction with the same amount of each element as you started with.
Balancing an equation	We have to make sure that the same number of atoms of each element appear on both sides of the equation without changing any correct formulae.
Example 1	iron + hydrochloric acid → iron (II) chloride + hydrogen.
Correct formulae	$Fe(s)$ + $HCl(aq)$ ⟶ $FeCl_2(aq)$ + $H_2(g)$ (unbalanced)

	LHS			*RHS*	
	Fe	1		Fe	1
	H	1		H	2
	Cl	1		Cl	2

Balancing the equation	To balance you need to adjust the number of molecules of a substance by putting a new number *in front*. Note that the number 1 is understood.

If a 2 is put in front of HCl you get:

$$Fe(S) + 2HCl\,(aq) \longrightarrow FeCl_2(aq) + H_2\,(g)$$
(balanced)

Example 2	iron (III) oxide + hydrogen → iron + steam.
Correct formulae	$Fe_2O_3(s) + H_2(g) \longrightarrow Fe(s) + H_2O(g)$
Balance O	$Fe_2O_3(s) + H_2(g) \longrightarrow Fe(s) + 3H_2O(g)$
Balance H	$Fe_2O_3(s) + 3H_2(g) \longrightarrow Fe(s) + 3H_2O(g)$
Balance Fe	$Fe_2O_3(s) + 3H_2(g) \longrightarrow 2\,Fe(s) + 3H_2O(g)$
	(balanced equation)
Example 3	sodium hydroxide + copper (II) nitrate ⟶ copper (II) hydroxide + sodium nitrate.
Correct formulae	$NaOH(aq) + Cu(NO_3)_2(aq) \rightarrow Cu(OH)_2(s) + NaNO_3(aq)$
Balance NO_3 group	$NaOH(aq) + Cu(NO_3)_2(aq) \rightarrow Cu(OH)_2(s) + 2NaNO_3(aq)$
Balance Na	$2NaOH(aq) + Cu(NO_3)_2(aq) \rightarrow Cu(OH)_2(s) + 2\,NaNO_3(aq)$
Check OH group and Cu	Both balanced – so equation is balanced.

6 Counting Atoms and Molecules

The Mole
(abbreviation
= mol)

The mole is the unit of quantity of atoms, molecules, ions, etc. It represents a very large number (6×10^{23}) and is:

the number of atoms in 1 g of hydrogen [$A_r(H) = 1$]

in 12 g of carbon [$A_r(C) = 12$]

or in the relative atomic mass in grams of any element;

or the number of molecules in 2 g of hydrogen, $H_2[M_r(H_2) = 2]$

in 18 g of water, $H_2O[M_r(H_2O) = 18]$

in 250 g of $CuSO_4$, $5H_2O$ ($M_r = 250$)

or in the relative formula mass in grams of any molecule.

We don't have to talk about exactly 1 mole of particles but can talk about any number of moles (small or large).

Example 1

0.2 mol of water molecules have a mass of (0.2×18) g = 3.6 g.
4 mol of $CuSO_4 .5H_2O$ molecules have a mass of
(4×250) g = 1000 g.
3.5 mol of H_2 molecules have a mass of (3.5×2) g = 7.0 g.

Example 2

1.8 g of water contain $\frac{1.8}{18}$ mol (= 0.1 mol) of water molecules.

10.0 g of hydrogen contain $\frac{10.0}{1}$ mol (= 10.0 mol) of hydrogen *atoms.*

$\frac{10.0}{2}$ mol (= 5.0 mol) of hydrogen *molecules.*

Problems using
Moles

Example 1

What is the mass of 1.5 mol of NaOH molecules?

$M_r(NaOH) = 23 + 16 + 1 = 40$
1 mol of NaOH molecules has a mass of 40 g ←————Always start
with a statement
of what you know.

∴1.5 mol have a mass of $(1.5 \times 40) = 60$ g

Example 2

What is the mass of 0.25 mol of H_2SO_4 molecules?

$M_r (H_2SO_4) = 2 + 32 + 64 = 98$
1 mol of H_2SO_4 molecules has a mass of 98 g
∴0.25 mol has a mass of $(0.25 \times 98) = 24.5$ g

Example 3

How many moles of FeS molecules are contained in 4.4 g FeS?

$M_r(FeS) = 56 + 32 = 88$
88 g of FeS is the mass of 1 mol
∴4.4 g of FeS is the mass of $\frac{4.4}{88} = 0.05$ mol

| Molar Volume | Molar volume is the volume occupied at a particular temperature and pressure by 1 mol of *any gas* particles. At room temperature and pressure (r.t.p.), the molar volume is 24 litres. |

Examples 1 mol of H_2 gas occupies a volume of 24 l at r.t.p.
0.5 mol of CO_2 gas occupies a volume of 12 l at r.t.p.

Formula from Mass Composition Given the mass of each element present in a compound, the formula may be found.

Example An oxide of copper is found to contain 8 g of copper combined with 1 g of oxygen [$A_r(Cu) = 64$, $A_r(O) = 16$]. What is the formula?

	Cu	O
Mass	8 g	1 g
No. mol	$\dfrac{8}{64}\,(= 0.125)$	$\dfrac{1}{16}\,(= 0.0625)$

Simplest ratio   Divide by the lowest number of moles:

$$\frac{0.125}{0.0625} = 2 \qquad\qquad \frac{0.0625}{0.0625} = 1$$

Mole ratio   Cu:O = 2:1

$\therefore$ Formula = Cu_2O

Note: This is the simplest formula (called the empirical formula). We would need to know the relative formula mass to determine the actual (molecular) formula.

Calculations Based on Equations In Chapter 5 we said that a chemical equation could be considered in terms of numbers of atoms, molecules, etc. Since a mole represents a very large fixed number of particles, we can also consider an equation in terms of moles.

Example

$$2Mg(s) \quad + \quad O_2(g) \quad \rightarrow \quad 2MgO(s)$$

2 mol Mg atoms	react with	1 mol O_2 molecules	to give	2 mol MgO molecules
[$A_r(Mg) = 24$]		[$M_r(O_2) = 32$]		[$M_r(MgO) = 24 + 16$ = 40]

$\therefore (2 \times 24)$ g Mg + 32 g O_2 $\rightarrow$ (2×40) g MgO

Note: The total mass of Mg and O_2 $(48 + 32 = 80$ g) is the same as the mass of MgO(80 g).

Calculations Based on Mass		
Example 1	What mass of magnesium oxide will be formed when 6 g of magnesium ribbon is burned completely in oxygen?	
Balanced equation	$2Mg(s) + O_2(g) \longrightarrow 2MgO(s)$	
What we know and need from equation in moles	2 mol Mg $\longrightarrow$ 2 mol MgO	We don't need to consider the amount of oxygen since it is in excess, i.e. more than enough.
Convert to masses	48 g Mg $\longrightarrow$ 80 g MgO	
What we are asked?	$\therefore$ 6 g Mg $\longrightarrow (80 \times \frac{6}{48})$ g MgO $\longrightarrow$ 10 g MgO	The fraction of Mg we take compared with our known 48 g $(\frac{6}{48})$ must be the same as the fraction of MgO we form.
Example 2	What mass of hydrogen will be formed when 0.092 g sodium reacts with excess water?	
Balanced equation	$2Na(s) + 2H_2O(l) \longrightarrow 2NaOH(aq) + H_2(g)$	
Equation moles	2 mol Na $\longrightarrow$ 1 mol H_2	H_2O is in excess and we're not asked about NaOH.
Convert to masses	46 g Na $\longrightarrow$ 2 g H_2 $\therefore$ 0.092 g Na $\longrightarrow (2 \times \frac{0.092}{46})$ g H_2 $\longrightarrow$ 0.004 g H_2	
Calculations Based on Volume	Since we know the volume occupied by 1 mole of any gas at r.t.p. is 24 l, we can involve volumes in calculations.	
Example	What volume of hydrogen will be formed at room temperature and pressure, if 3 g magnesium reacts with hydrochloric acid?	
Balanced equation	$Mg(s) + 2HCl(aq) \longrightarrow MgCl_2(aq) + H_2(g)$	

Equation in moles	1 mol Mg $\longrightarrow$ 1 mol H_2
Convert to mass or vol as needed	24 g Mg $\longrightarrow$ 24 l H_2
	$\therefore$ 3 g Mg $\longrightarrow$ $(24 \times \frac{3}{24})$ l H_2
	$\longrightarrow$ 3 l H_2 at r.t.p.

Concentration of Solutions

The concentration of a solution is expressed as:

or
- grams in 1 l of solution (g/l),
- moles in 1 l of solution (mol/l).

It doesn't matter how much solution we have since, to write the concentration, we scale up (or down) to a volume of 1 l, i.e. we write down how many grams or moles would be contained in 1 litre of solution of the same concentration.

Example

1 g of NaOH in 100 cm^3 solution is equivalent to:

$(1 \times \frac{1000}{100})$ g NaOH in $100 \times \frac{1000}{100} (= 1000$ cm^3) solution (or 1 l)

that is to say, 10 g NaOH in 1 l

$\therefore$ concentration of NaOH = 10 g/l

Converting g/l to mol/l

Since the relative formula mass in grams is the mass of 1 mole, g/l can be converted to mol/l by dividing by M_r. Thus, from the above example:

Concentration of NaOH = 10 g/l

$= \frac{10}{40}$ mol/l   [M_r(NaOH) = 40]

$= 0.25$ mol/l

Example

25 g H_2SO_4 is contained in 5 l of solution. What is the concentration in (a) g/l, (b) mol/l?

25 g H_2SO_4 in 5 l is equivalent to $\frac{25}{5}$ g H_2SO_4 in 1 l

$\therefore$ concentration of H_2SO_4 = 5 g/l

$= \frac{5}{98}$ mol/l   [M_r(H_2SO_4) = 98]

$= 0.051$ mol/l

Concentration from Titration Results

Results from a titration will usually consist of:

(a) a certain volume of one solution of known concentration which is neutralised by

(b) a known volume of a second solution of unknown concentration.

(The solution of unknown concentration may be either that in the burette or that measured out exactly in advance into a conical flask).

Example 1   20 cm^3 of hydrochloric acid (concentration 0.2 mol/l) was needed to neutralise 25 cm^3 of sodium hydroxide solution. What is the concentration of NaOH in mol/l?

No. of mol of solution of known concentration

mol HCl in 1000 cm^3 solution = 0.2 (by definition)

∴ mol HCl in 20cm^3 solution $= 0.2 \times \dfrac{20}{1000} = 0.004$ mol

Balanced equation

HCl(aq) + NaOH(aq) → NaCl(aq) + H$_2$O(l)

Mole ratio   ∴ 1 mol HCl reacts with 1 mol NaOH

No. mol of solution of unknown conc.

∴ mol NaOH (in 25 cm^3) reacting with the 0.004 mol HCl

= 0.004

(since the no. of moles of NaOH and HCl reacting must always be the same.)

Mol in 1000 cm^3

∴ mol NaOH in 1000 cm^3 $= 0.004 \times \dfrac{1000}{25}$

∴ concentration of NaOH = 0.16 mol/l

Example 2   15 cm^3 of sulphuric acid was needed to neutralise 10 cm^3 of potassium hydroxide solution (concentration 0.1 mol/l). What is the concentration of H$_2$SO$_4$ in mol/l?

Mol KOH (known conc.)

mol KOH in 1000 cm^3 solution = 0.1

∴ mol KOH in 10 cm^3 solution $= 0.1 \times \dfrac{10}{1000} = 0.001$ mol

Balanced equation

H$_2$SO$_4$(aq) + 2KOH(aq) → K$_2$SO$_4$(aq) + 2H$_2$O(l)

Mole ratio   1 mol H$_2$SO$_4$ reacts with 2 mol KOH

Mol H$_2$SO$_4$ (unknown conc.)

∴ mol H$_2$SO$_4$ (in 15cm^3) reacting with the 0.001 mol KOH

$= 0.001 \times \frac{1}{2} = 0.0005$ mol

(since no. of moles of H$_2$SO$_4$ is always half the no. of moles of KOH → mole ratio = 1:2)

Mol in 1000 cm^3

∴ mol H$_2$SO$_4$ in 1000 cm^3 $= 0.0005 \times \dfrac{1000}{15}$

∴ concentration of H$_2$SO$_4$ = 0.033 mol/l

7 Electrochemistry

Electrolyte	An electrolyte is a liquid which conducts electricity and contains positively and negatively charged ions.
Electric Current	An electric current is a flow of electrons in a metal or a movement of ions towards a charged rod in an electrolyte.

Conductors (1)
Solid metals
Liquid metals   } conducting, due to free moving electrons.
Graphite

Examples   Cu, Fe, mercury.

Conductors (2)
Molten ionic substances
Ionic substances in aqueous solution   } conducting, due to free moving ions.

Examples   NaCl(l), NaCl(aq).

Non-conductors
Gaseous metals   – not conducting, due to no free moving electrons.

Solid ionic compounds   – ions fixed in lattice, so not free to move.

Covalent compounds   – no ions.

Electrolysis	Electrolysis is a process where electrical energy is used to decompose an electrolyte.
Electrodes	Electrodes are conducting rods dipping into electrolyte.

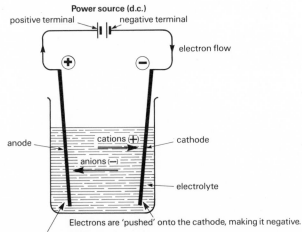

Power source (d.c.)
positive terminal · negative terminal
electron flow
anode — cations ⊕ — cathode
anions ⊖
electrolyte
Electrons are 'pushed' onto the cathode, making it negative.
Electrons are 'pulled' off the anode, making it positive.

Anode	The positive electrode is called the anode.
Cathode	The negative electrode is called the cathode.
Anions	Anions are negative (–) ions attracted towards the positive anode (+).
Cations	Cations are positive (+) ions attracted towards the negative cathode (–).
Electrolysis of Molten Sodium Chloride	
Ions present	Na$^+$ and Cl$^-$.
Cathode reaction	The Na$^+$ ions are attracted to the cathode (–) where they gain electrons.

$$Na^+(l) + e^- \rightarrow Na(l)$$

Sodium metal is discharged at the cathode.

Anode reaction	The Cl$^-$ ions are attracted to the anode (+) where they lose electrons.

$$Cl^-(l) - e^- \rightarrow Cl(g) \text{ but Cl atoms cannot exist on their own.}$$

$$Cl(g) + Cl(g) \rightarrow Cl_2(g)$$

Chlorine gas is discharged at the anode.

Overall change	$2NaCl(l) \rightarrow 2Na(l) + Cl_2(g)$
Electrolysis of Aluminium Oxide (Al$_2$O$_3$)	
Industrial importance	Aluminium metal, used a lot in industry, is obtained by electrolysis.
Source of Al$_2$O$_3$	The ore bauxite is mined and purified before use.
Electrodes	Carbon electrodes are used.
Electrolyte	The purified bauxite is dissolved in the molten liquid of another aluminium ore, cryolite, at 900°C.
Ions present	Al^{3+} and O^{2-}.
Cathode reaction	Al^{3+} ions are attracted to the cathode (–) where they gain electrons.

$$Al^{3+}(l) + 3e^- \rightarrow Al(l)$$

Anode reaction	O^{2-} ions are attracted to the anode (+) where they lose electrons.

$$O^{2-}(l) - 2e^- \rightarrow O(g) \text{ but O atoms cannot exist on their own.}$$

$$O(g) + O(g) \rightarrow O_2(g)$$

Overall change	$2Al_2O_3(l) \rightarrow 4Al(l) + 3O_2(g)$
Source of power	Since large amounts of electricity are needed for this industrial process, the manufacturing plant is sited near a power station or hydro-electric generator.

Electrolysis of Brine NaCl(aq)

Brine	Brine is a concentrated solution of sodium chloride in water.
Ions present	$Na^+(aq)$ (from brine) and $H^+(aq)$ (from water) $Cl^-(aq)$ (from brine) and $OH^-(aq)$ (from water)
Competition between ions	When more than one ion of a particular charge is present, both may be attracted to an electrode, but only one gains or loses electrons and is discharged.
Cathode reaction	$H^+(aq)$ ions gain electrons. (Na^+ ions need much more energy.) $H^+(aq) + e^- \rightarrow H(g)$ $H(g) + H(g) \rightarrow H_2(g)$
Anode reaction	$Cl^-(aq)$ ions lose electrons. $Cl^-(aq) - e^- \rightarrow Cl(g)$ $Cl(g) + Cl(g) \rightarrow Cl_2(g)$
Useful products	H_2 can be used in the food industry (see page 87). Cl_2 is used for several purposes (see page 67).

Electrolysis of Acidified Water (or Dilute Sulphuric Acid)

	Pure water does not produce enough ions for it to conduct, so some dilute sulphuric acid is added.
Ions present from water	H^+ and OH^-.
Anode reaction	$OH^-(aq) - e^- \longrightarrow OH$ $OH + OH \longrightarrow H_2O + O$ $O + O \longrightarrow O_2(g)$ ――――――――――――――― (overall) $4OH^-(aq) - 4e^- \rightarrow O_2(g) + 2H_2O$
Cathode reaction	$H^+(aq) + e^- \longrightarrow H$ $H + H \longrightarrow H_2(g)$ or $4H^+(aq) + 4e^- \longrightarrow 2H_2(g)$ (So same number of e^- are gained by H^+ as lost by OH^-)

Volume ratio $O_2:H_2$	$\text{mol } O_2 : \text{mol } H_2 = 1 : 2$ $\therefore \text{vol. } O_2 : \text{vol. } H_2 = 1 : 2$ In practice, the volume of oxygen formed is *less* than half that of hydrogen, since oxygen is slightly soluble in water.
Electrolysis of Copper Chloride Solution	
(a) Using inert (e.g. carbon) electrodes	
Ions present from $CuCl_2$	Cu^{2+} and Cl^-.
Cathode reaction	$Cu^{2+}(aq) + 2e^- \rightarrow Cu(s)$ Red-brown copper is deposited on the cathode and the solution will become less blue.
Anode reaction	$2Cl^-(aq) - 2e^- \rightarrow Cl_2(g)$
(b) Using copper electrodes	
Cathode reaction	Cu metal will be deposited, as above.
Anode reaction	It requires less energy to dissolve the copper anode than it does to discharge the chlorine. $Cu(s) - 2e \rightarrow Cu^{2+}(aq)$ (The solution will keep the same blue intensity, since the same no. of moles of Cu^{2+} are formed as are used up.)
Electrolysis of Copper Sulphate Solution	
Cathode reaction	Copper is deposited with either inert or copper electrodes.
Anode reaction	*Inert electrode* – oxygen gas discharged as with the electrolysis of acidified water. *Copper electrode* – dissolves, as with copper chloride.
Refining of Impure Copper	
Cathode	The cathode is a rod of pure copper.

Anode	The anode is the impure copper.
Electrolyte	The electrolyte is copper sulphate solution.
Cathode reaction	Cu^{2+} ions are converted to Cu metal, deposited on the pure copper rod.
Anode reaction	The copper from the impure copper is converted to Cu^{2+} ions at the same rate as the pure copper is deposited at the cathode.
Anode sludge	The impurities which collect below the anode are called anode sludge.

Electrolysis of Hydrochloric Acid

Cathode reaction	$2H^+(aq) + 2e^- \rightarrow H_2(g)$
Anode reaction	$2Cl^-(aq) - 2e^- \rightarrow Cl_2(g)$

Electroplating	Metal objects can be plated with a thin layer of another metal by applying the principles of electrolysis.
Metal object	The metal object is connected as the cathode of the cell.
Electrolyte	The electrolyte must contain the metal ions of the metal to be coated.
Examples	Chromium plating, nickel plating, silver plating (Compare anodising of aluminium on page 65.)

General Rules on Electrolysis

Metal ions, Hydrogen ions	The metal ions (and the hydrogen ions) are attracted to the cathode and discharged there as the metal (or H_2).
Non-metal ions (except H^+ ions)	Non-metal ions are attracted to the anode and discharged as a gas at the anode.
Choice of products	At a particular electrode, the ion which gains or loses electrons is the one which requires the least amount of energy.

8 Acids, Bases and Salts

Acids and Bases	
Acids	Acids produce H^+ ions in water solution.
H^+ ions	H^+ ions are protons. (An H atom contains one proton and one electron, and loses its electron on forming an H^+ ion.)
Donors	Acids are defined as proton donors.
Donation to bases	Acids donate protons to bases.
Examples	Hydrochloric acid, HCl Nitric acid, HNO_3 Sulphuric acid, H_2SO_4 Citric acid Ethanoic (acetic) acid, CH_3COOH
Bases	Bases are defined as proton acceptors.
Alkalis	Alkalis are bases which are soluble in water.

Examples

Alkalis	Insoluble bases
sodium hydroxide, NaOH potassium hydroxide, KOH ammonium hydroxide, NH_4OH calcium hydroxide, $Ca(OH)_2$	copper (II) oxide, CuO zinc oxide, ZnO iron (II) hydroxide, $Fe(OH)_2$ iron (III) hydroxide, $Fe(OH)_3$ and other metal oxides and metal hydroxides

Acid/Base Reaction

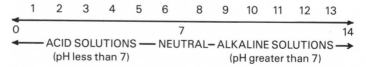

proton donor   proton acceptor

$$HCl(aq) + NaOH(aq) \rightarrow NaCl(aq) + H_2O(l)$$

donates H^+

pH Scale The pH scale measures the strength of acids and alkalis. It is based on the amount of H^+ ions in an acid solution and amount of OH^- ions in an alkaline solution.

```
     1   2   3   4   5   6     8   9   10  11  12  13
   ◄─────────────────────────────────────────────────►
   0                         7                        14
   ◄───── ACID SOLUTIONS ─── NEUTRAL─ ALKALINE SOLUTIONS ──►
         (pH less than 7)            (pH greater than 7)
```

Since the value of pH depends on the number of H^+ ions and OH^- ions in solution, it depends on the extent of ionisation of the acid or alkali, in other words the proportion of the molecules in solution which separate into ions.

Strong Acids	Strong acids are acids which are strongly ionised and have a pH near 1 or 0.
Examples	$HCl(aq)$, $HNO_3(aq)$, or $H_2SO_4(aq)$.
Weak Acids	Weak acids are acids which are partially ionised in solution and have a pH near 4 or 5.
Examples	Citric acid, ethanoic acid.
Strong Alkalis	Strong alkalis are alkalis which are strongly ionised and have a pH near 14.
Examples	$NaOH(aq)$, $KOH(aq)$.
Weak Alkalis	Weak alkalis are alkalis which are weakly ionised and have a pH near 10.
Examples	$NH_4OH(aq)$, $Ca(OH)_2(aq)$.

> Note: In order to compare the pH of solutions, one must be considering solutions of the same concentration.

Neutralisation Neutralisation is a reaction where an acid reacts completely with an alkali to form a salt and water:

$$\frac{\text{nitric}}{\text{acid}} + \frac{\text{potassium}}{\text{hydroxide}} \rightarrow \frac{\text{potassium}}{\text{nitrate}} + \text{water}$$

$$HNO_3(aq) + KOH(aq) \rightarrow KNO_3(aq) + H_2O(l)$$

In the solution each of the chemicals except water ionises completely. We can write:

$$H^+(aq) + NO_3^-(aq) + K^+(aq) + OH(aq)$$
$$\rightarrow K^+(aq) + NO_3^-(aq) + H_2O(l)$$

In a reaction we are really interested in those parts which undergo a change.

Spectator ions Spectator ions are ions, like K^+ and NO_3^- in the above reaction, which are present in solution *both* at the start *and* at the end of the reaction.

Ionic equation The ionic equation of the reaction is the equation showing the ions undergoing a change in the reaction, and the products – but omitting the spectator ions.

Ionic equation for any neutralisation reaction

$$H^+(aq) + OH^-(aq) \rightarrow H_2O(l)$$
(from acid)   (from alkali)

This equation applies to *any* neutralisation reaction.

Indicators Indicators are substances which are a different colour in acid and alkaline solutions. They are used to enable us to detect when an alkali is exactly neutralised by an acid (or vice versa) – as in a titration.

Examples	Colour in alkaline solution	Colour in acidic solution
universal indicator	blue	red
litmus	blue	red
methyl orange	yellow	pink

Titration Titration is a practical procedure used to determine the exact volume of an acid reacting with a known volume of alkali.

Burette,
Pipette,
Conical flask

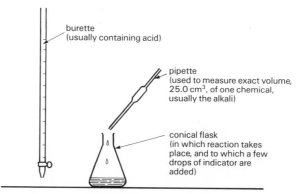

burette
(usually containing acid)

pipette
(used to measure exact volume, 25.0 cm³, of one chemical, usually the alkali)

conical flask
(in which reaction takes place, and to which a few drops of indicator are added)

Procedure
1. Acid is added to rinse the burette and run out. More acid is added until liquid level is just below zero line.

2. Pipette is rinsed with small amount of alkali, using pipette filler, and run out. Exactly 25 cm³ of the alkali is measured and run into the conical flask. (Alternatively, exactly 25 cm³ of alkali could be measured with a second burette.)

3. Two or three drops of indicator are added to the alkali in the flask.

4. The liquid level on the burette is read and recorded. Acid is then added to the alkali until the indicator *just* changes colour (adding a drop at a time near the end-point).

5. A second reading of the burette is taken.

6. The procedure is repeated until consistent readings are obtained.

Calculations The results from the titration are used to determine the concentration of one of the two solutions as shown in Chapter 6.

Reactions of Acids

Alkalis Alkalis neutralise acids.

Metals Metals generally react with acids to give off hydrogen gas. (The metals have to be fairly reactive.)

39

Examples   iron + $\dfrac{\text{hydrochloric}}{\text{acid}}$ → $\dfrac{\text{iron (II)}}{\text{chloride}}$ + hydrogen

$Fe(s) + 2HCl(aq) \longrightarrow FeCl_2(aq) + H_2(g)$

Other metals reacting like this include magnesium, zinc and aluminium.

> Note: Copper does *not* react with acids to release hydrogen.

Insoluble Metal Oxides and Metal Hydroxides   These are bases and so react with acids to form a salt and water.

Examples $\dfrac{\text{copper}}{\text{oxide}}$ + $\dfrac{\text{sulphuric}}{\text{acid}}$ → $\dfrac{\text{copper}}{\text{sulphate}}$ + water

$CuO(s) + H_2SO_4(aq) \rightarrow CuSO_4(aq) + H_2O(l)$

Metal Carbonates and Hydrogen Carbonates   These react with acids to form carbon dioxide, water and a metal salt.

Examples $\dfrac{\text{sodium}}{\text{carbonate}}$ + $\dfrac{\text{nitric}}{\text{acid}}$ $\longrightarrow$ $\dfrac{\text{sodium}}{\text{nitrate}}$ + $\dfrac{\text{carbon}}{\text{dioxide}}$ + water

$Na_2CO_3(l) + 2HNO_3(aq) \rightarrow 2NaNO_3(aq) + CO_2(g) + H_2O(l)$

Reaction of Alkalis

Acids   Acids react with alkalis to form a salt and water.

Metal salt solutions   Metal salt solutions often react with the OH^- ions from an alkali to form an insoluble metal hydroxide, as a precipitate (ppt), which is a solid formed in a reaction on mixing together two solutions.

Example $FeSO_4(aq) + 2NaOH(aq) \rightarrow Fe(OH)_2 (s) + Na_2SO_4(aq)$
                                                    green ppt

Ionic equation $Fe^{2+}(aq) + 2OH^-(aq) \rightarrow Fe(OH)_2(s)$

Further examples $Al^{3+}(aq) + 3OH^-(aq) \rightarrow Al(OH)_3(s)$ white ppt

$Cu^{2+}(aq) + 2OH^-(aq) \rightarrow Cu(OH)_2(s)$ pale-blue ppt

$Fe^{3+}(aq) + 3OH^-(aq) \rightarrow Fe(OH)_3(s)$ red-brown ppt
from iron (III) salts

> Note: A Data Book can be used to check the solubility of different metal hydroxides. It is provided in some exams.

Everyday Substances

Acidic substances   Acidic substances include vinegar (containing ethanoic acid), soda water (carbon dioxide in water), fruit juices (containing citric acid), acid rain.

Alkaline substances   Alkaline substances include domestic ammonia solution, milk of magnesia (for neutralising the excess stomach acid in indigestion), lime (for neutralising acid soils).

Salts   Salts are composed of two ions.

Examples

Salt	Positive ion from parent base	Parent base	Negative ion from parent acid	Parent acid
$NaNO_3$	Na^+	$NaOH$	NO_3^-	HNO_3
$CuSO_4$	Cu^{2+}	CuO or $Cu(OH)_2$	SO_4^{2-}	H_2SO_4
NH_4Cl	NH_4^+	NH_4OH	Cl^-	HCl
$Fe_2(SO_4)_3$	Fe^{3+}	Fe_2O_3 or $Fe(OH)_3$	SO_4^{2-}	H_2SO_4

> Note: Although we say that a salt is based on a parent base and a parent acid, we do not necessarily make it by reacting these two.

Preparation of Salts   There are several different methods which can be used in the laboratory for the preparation of salts, but several factors need to be considered before deciding which method to use to prepare a particular salt.

Factors to be considered   Solubility of salt ⎫ Look in your Data Book, if your
Solubility of the base ⎭ syllabus allows you to use one.
Safety

Direct Combination of Elements   Direct combination can be used to make a salt composed of two elements only.

Example 1   *Iron (II) sulphide.*
Iron metal is heated with sulphur:

$$Fe(s) + S(s) \rightarrow FeS(s)$$

Example 2   *Iron (III) chloride.*
Iron metal heated in a stream of chlorine gas:

$$2Fe(s) + 3Cl_2(g) \rightarrow 2FeCl_3(s)$$

Dilute Acid and Metal	Dilute acid and a metal can be used
	(a) if the metal will react with the acid; and
	(b) if the reaction can be carried out safely.
Example	*Zinc chloride.*
	Zinc added to dilute hydrochloric acid:
	$Zn(s) + 2HCl(aq) \rightarrow ZnCl_2(aq) + H_2(g)$
Dilute Acid and Insoluble Base	Dilute acid and an insoluble base can be used
	(a) if the salt is soluble; and
	(b) if the positive ion is not Na^+, K^+, Ca^{2+}, NH_4^+.
Example 1	*Copper sulphate.*
	Copper (II) oxide added to dilute sulphuric acid:
	$CuO(s) + H_2SO_4(aq) \rightarrow CuSO_4(aq) + H_2O(l)$
Example 2	*Iron (III) nitrate.*
	Iron (III) hydroxide added to dilute nitric acid:
	$Fe(OH)_3(s) + 3HNO_3(aq) \rightarrow Fe(NO_3)_3 + 3H_2O(l)$
Dilute Acid and Insoluble Metal Carbonate	Dilute acid and an insoluble metal carbonate can be used
	(a) if the salt is soluble; and
	(b) if the positive ion is not Na^+, K^+, NH_4^+.
Example	*Copper (II) sulphate.*
	Copper (II) carbonate is added to dilute sulphuric acid:
	$CuCO_3(s) + H_2SO_4(aq) \rightarrow CuSO_4(aq) + CO_2(g) + H_2O(l)$
	Instead of metal carbonate, a metal hydrogencarbonate can be used.
Dilute Acid and an Alkali	Dilute acid and an alkali is the reaction already described as a titration. But how does one obtain a salt which is not contaminated with the indicator?
	The normal titration (with indicator) is performed.
	The titration is repeated without the indicator, but the same volume of acid is added from the burette.
Precipitation	Precipitation, as a method, can only be used to make an insoluble salt. You need to mix two solutions, each of which contains one of the ions needed in the salt.
Example	To make insoluble barium sulphate (containing Ba^{2+} ions and SO_4^{2-} ions), mix:
	Ba^{2+} ions from $BaCl_2$ solution or $Ba(NO_3)_2$ solution
	with
	SO_4^{2-} ions from H_2SO_4 solution or Na_2SO_4 solution.

The equation is:

$$BaCl_2(aq) + H_2SO_4(aq) \rightarrow BaSO_4(s) + 2HCl(aq)$$

$$Ba^{2+}(aq) + SO_4^{2-}(aq) \rightarrow BaSO_4(s) \text{ (ionic equation)}$$

Practical Notes

Pure Solution A pure solution of a salt is obtained when using a method involving the reaction of a solid with a solution by adding solid to the solution until no more reaction occurs, i.e. some of the solid remains unreacted. This can then be filtered to leave a filtrate of the pure salt solution.

Pure Crystals Pure crystals can be obtained by evaporating the pure salt solution carefully until a saturated solution is obtained, and then leaving it to cool, when crystals will form.

Choosing a Method

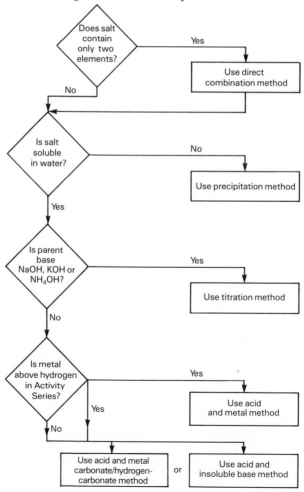

43

9 | Oxidation and Reduction

Reactions 1 Reactions, in simple terms, can be divided into two types. Firstly, those where there is an exchange of ionic partners, like most of the ones met so far in this book.

Example $Ag^+NO_3^-(aq) + Na^+Cl^-(aq) \rightarrow Ag^+Cl^-(s) + Na^+NO_3^-(aq)$

Sometimes, there is a slight rearrangement of a product. For instance, when an acid reacts with a carbonate:

$$2H^+(aq) + CO_3^{2-} \rightarrow H_2CO_3 \text{ (carbonic acid)}.$$

The carbonic acid, in practice, decomposes to form H_2O and CO_2.

Reactions 2 Secondly, those reactions where there is an exchange of electrons.

Example $Mg(s) + 2H^+(aq) \rightarrow Mg^{2+}(aq) + H_2(g)$

loses 2e⁻   gains 2e⁻

Reactions like this are classified as oxidation/reduction (or redox).

Oxidation and Reduction These are processes in which any combination of the following changes takes place.

Oxidation	Reduction
electrons are lost; and/or oxygen is gained; and/or hydrogen is lost	electrons are gained; and/or oxygen is lost; and/or hydrogen is gained

Oxidation and reduction must take place *simultaneously* into a reaction, i.e. if one chemical loses oxygen atoms, another chemical must gain them (Law of Conservation of Mass).

Example 1 $2Mg(s) + O_2(g) \longrightarrow 2MgO(s)$

Mg half-reaction $2Mg - 4e^- \longrightarrow 2Mg^{2+}$

(2,8,2)   each Mg   (2,8)   *oxidation*
             loses 2e

O half-reaction $O_2 + 4e^- \longrightarrow 2O^{2-}$

(2,6)   each O   (2,8)   *reduction*
             gains 2e⁻

Summary The magnesium is oxidised by the oxygen to magnesium ion and the oxygen is reduced by the magnesium to the oxide ion.

Example 2	$CuO(s) + H_2(g) \rightarrow Cu(s) + H_2O(l)$

Cu
half-reaction

$Cu^{2+} + 2e^- \rightarrow Cu$ *reduction*

or copper oxide loses oxygen to form copper *reduction*

and hydrogen gains oxygen to form water *oxidation*

Summary: The copper in copper oxide is reduced to copper metal and the hydrogen is oxidised to water.

> Note: The oxygen is present in combined form in both CuO and H_2O, and so is basically unchanged in the reaction.

Example 3 $2KI(aq) + Cl_2(aq) \rightarrow 2KCl(aq) + I_2(aq)$

Spectator ion: K^+ in KI stays as K^+ in KCl.

Ionic equation: $2I^-(aq) + Cl_2(aq) \rightarrow 2Cl^-(aq) + I_2(aq)$

I
half-reaction

$2I^- - 2e^- \rightarrow I_2$ so, *oxidation*
loses electrons

Cl
half-reaction

$Cl_2 + 2e^- \rightarrow 2Cl^-$ so, *reduction*
gains electrons

Summary: Iodine in I^- is oxidised to I_2 by chlorine and chlorine is reduced to Cl^- by the iodide ions.

> Note: In this example there is no oxygen or hydrogen involved.

Example 4 *Electrolysis of acidified water*

Cathode reaction:
$2H^+(aq) + 2e^- \rightarrow H_2(g)$
gain of electrons, so *reduction*

Anode reaction:
$4OH^-(aq) - 2e^- \rightarrow O_2(g) + 2H_2O(l)$
loss of e^-, so *oxidation*

All electrolysis processes are examples of redox reactions:

cathode reaction is *always reduction*,

anode reaction is *always oxidation*.

Example 5 *Conversion of Fe(s) to Fe^{3+} (aq).*

Half-reaction:
$Fe(s) - 3e^- \rightarrow Fe^{3+}(s)$
loss of e^-, so *oxidation*

Example in nature: When iron objects rust, the metal is oxidised to Fe^{3+} in the air (in the presence of moisture).

Equation:
$4Fe(s) + 3O_2(aq) \rightarrow 2Fe_2O_3(s)$
(simplified equation)

Example 6 *Conversion of Fe^{2+} (aq) to Fe^{3+} (aq).*

Half-reaction Fe^{2+} (aq) $-$ e^- $\rightarrow$ Fe^{3+} (aq)

loss of e^-, so *oxidation*

When compounds containing Fe^{2+} ions are left exposed to air, they are readily oxidized to Fe^{3+}. For instance:

$$Fe(OH)_2(s) \xrightarrow[\text{air}]{\text{exposure to}} Fe(OH)_3(s)$$
greenish ppt.   red-brown ppt.
(not balanced)

Oxidising and Reducing Agents

Oxidising agents
Oxidising agents are chemicals which oxidise another chemical.

Oxidising

Example
Iron is rusted to iron (III) oxide by oxygen, so the oxidising agent is oxygen.

Reducing agents
Reducing agents are chemicals which reduce another chemical.

Example
$CuO(s) + H_2(g) \rightarrow Cu(s) + H_2O(l)$

The H_2 is reducing the copper (in CuO) to copper metal, so the reducing agent is hydrogen.

Other Examples

Example 1
$Cl_2(aq) + 2I^-(aq) \rightarrow I_2(aq) + 2Cl^-(aq)$

Oxidising agent
The I^- is oxidised to I_2 (loss of e^-) so the oxidising agent is chlorine.

Reducing agent
The Cl_2 is reduced to Cl^- (gain of e^-) so the reducing agent is the iodide ion (or potassium iodide).

Example 2
Blast furnace.
When iron ore (Fe_2O_3) is converted to Fe metal in the reaction with carbon monoxide (see page 63).

$Fe_2O_3(s) + 3CO(g) \rightarrow 2Fe(l) + 3CO_2(g)$
reduced ⎯⎯ oxidised

Reducing agent	The carbon monoxide is reducing the Fe^{3+} (in Fe_2O_3) to Fe, so the reducing agent is carbon monoxide.
Example 3	*Combustion reactions.* In any reaction where a fuel is burned in oxygen, the fuel is oxidised, so oxygen is the oxidising agent.
Burning of Methane	$CH_4(g) + 2O_2(g) \rightarrow CO_2(g) + 2H_2O(l)$
Fire Triangle	All three are needed for combustion. This would apply to any combustion reaction.

Common Oxidising Agents	$O_2(g)$, $Cl_2(g)$, $Cl_2(aq)$, conc. H_2SO_4.
Common Reducing Agents	$H_2(g)$, metals, carbon, $KI(aq)$.

Note: Since an oxidising agent causes another substance to be oxidised (i.e. lose electrons), it itself must gain those electrons (and so be reduced).

Similarly, a reducing agent causes another substance to be reduced (i.e. gain electrons), so it itself must lose electrons (i.e. be oxidised).

Oxidising agents themselves always undergo reduction.

Reducing agents themselves always undergo oxidation.

---

10 Air

Gases in Dry Air

The gases which exist in dry air are nitrogen, oxygen, and small amounts of carbon dioxide, neon and argon.

Determination of volume composition

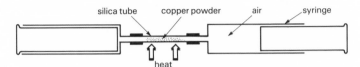

A known volume of air is passed back and forth between two syringes over some heated copper powder in a silicon tube until on cooling, there is no further change in volume. The reduction in volume represents the loss of oxygen.

Volume composition

The volume composition of dry air is:
nitrogen 78%, oxygen 21%, other gases 1%.

Carbon dioxide in air

Carbon dioxide in air can be shown by blowing air from a syringe or bicycle pump through lime-water, to see if it turns cloudy.

Water in air

Water in air can be shown by leaving out in the air some white copper (II) sulphate to see if it turns blue. (Blue cobalt chloride could be used and would turn pink.)

Separation of Air

Air can be separated by fractional distillation, after first liquefying it. Oxygen boils at $-183°C$, nitrogen boils at $-196°C$. Which boils first? Bear in mind that $-196°C$ is a lower temperature than $-183°C$. The answer is nitrogen, because N_2 has a lower relative formula mass ($M_r = 28$) than O_2 ($M_r = 32$).

Respiration

Glucose

Glucose is oxidised by oxygen to carbon dioxide and water, and the process releases chemical energy.

glucose + oxygen → carbon dioxide + water + chemical energy

Exhaled air

| | reduced by 5% | increased to 4% | increased to 1% | nitrogen etc. |

Combustion

Combustion occurs when substances burn in air.

Magnesium $2Mg(s) + O_2(g) \rightarrow 2MgO(s)$

Carbon $C(s) + O_2(g) \rightarrow CO_2(g)$ (complete combustion)

Sulphur $S(s) + O_2(g) \rightarrow SO_2(g)$

Fossil fuels   coal $\rightarrow CO_2(g)$ (complete combustion)

others $\rightarrow CO_2(g) + H_2O(g)$

Air pollution

Common pollutants	The most common air pollutants are carbon monoxide, sulphur dioxide, oxides of nitrogen, lead compounds, dust particles, unburnt hydrocarbons.

Carbon monoxide
Carbon monoxide results from the incomplete combustion of fuels such as petrol.

When fuels burn there is rarely enough oxygen for complete combustion. The following equations show what happens.

$$\text{Incomplete combustion: } C(s) + \tfrac{1}{2}O_2(g) \rightarrow CO(g)$$

$$\text{Complete combustion: } \quad C(s) + O_2(g) \rightarrow CO_2(g)$$

That is to say, twice as much oxygen is needed for complete combustion.

Carbon monoxide is highly toxic, and is absorbed by haemoglobin in blood. To prevent pollution, smoke-free zones, catalytic oxidisers, more effective burners, engines, etc. are needed.

Sulphur dioxide
Sulphur dioxide pollution comes from sulphur contained in fossil fuels.

$$S(s) + O_2(g) \rightarrow SO_2(g)$$

It is a lung irritant. It dissolves in water vapour to form acid-rain. Sulphur dioxide pollution can be prevented by careful removal of sulphur from fuels at refineries.

Oxides of nitrogen
Oxides of nitrogen are released by burning fossil fuels. These fuels were once living plants, which contained proteins containing nitrogen.

The oxides are respiratory irritants; they also dissolve in water vapour to form acid rain. Pollution can be prevented by removal of the nitrogen at oil refineries.

Lead compounds
Lead compound pollution comes from petrol engines, since some petrol still has lead compounds added to make engines run smoothly (to prevent 'knocking'). Lead compounds are removed from the engine in exhaust fumes. These compounds are harmful, particularly to the health of children. Lead pollution can be avoided by using unleaded petrol (green pump).

Dust particles
Dust particles come from many sources.

Unburnt hydrocarbons
Inefficient petrol engines emit unburnt hydrocarbons. This is a costly waste of energy and is harmful to health. Such pollution can be prevented by more efficient engines.

11 Water

Water Cycle	The sun's heat converts water from rivers and oceans to vapour in the atmosphere, where it condenses to fall as rain on land before draining into streams and rivers on its way back to the seas and oceans. In this way, water is conserved.

Natural Water

Sea Waters	Sea waters contain sodium chloride, magnesium compounds and bromides, which can be shown by evaporation and analysis.
Land Waters	Land waters contain minerals, many of which are beneficial to humans.
Hard Water	Hard water contains considerable amounts of Ca^{2+} and Mg^{2+} ions.
Advantages	It is good for bones, teeth and for reducing heart disease.
Disadvantages	1. It requires a lot of soap to form a lather.
	2. It leaves a scum after washing.
	3. It causes kettles to scale.
	4. It 'furs' pipes, by forming a deposit on the inside, reducing the bore.
Composition	$Ca(HCO_3)_2$ and other salts.
Characteristics	$Ca(HCO_3)_2$ decomposes on heating:

$$Ca(HCO_3)_2(aq) \rightarrow CaCO_3(s) + CO_2(g) + H_2O(l).$$

It is the insoluble $CaCO_3$ which forms the 'fur' on pipes and kettles.

Hard water is caused by rainwater (containing carbon dioxide) passing over and reacting with limestone rocks and dissolving small amounts of other rocks.

Soft Water	Soft water is water containing only small amounts of Ca^{2+} or Mg^{2+} ions which does not have the advantages or disadvantages of hard water.
Aerated Water	Aerated water is water containing dissolved oxygen from air. It is essential to life in water (i.e. plant and fish life).
Water Softening	Water softening involves the removal of the Ca^{2+} ions from the water.
	It is achieved by the following means.
	1. Distillation – leaves dissolved solids in the flask.
	2. Using extra soap.

3. Adding a chemical softener, such as washing soda $Na_2CO_3.10H_2O$.

The Na_2CO_3 reacts with Ca^{2+} to form insoluble $CaCO_3$.

$$Na_2CO_3(aq) + Ca^{2+}(aq) \rightarrow CaCO_3(s) + 2Na^+(aq)$$

4. Using ion exchange.

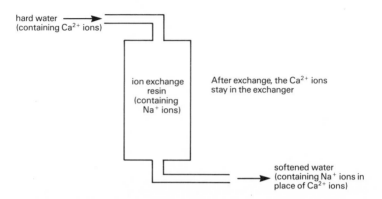

hard water
(containing Ca^{2+} ions)

ion exchange resin
(containing Na^+ ions)

After exchange, the Ca^{2+} ions stay in the exchanger

softened water
(containing Na^+ ions in place of Ca^{2+} ions)

The hard water is passed through a chemical in a column where the unwanted Ca^{2+} ions are exchanged for Na^+ ions. (If pure water is wanted a special chemical is used to exchange all cations for H^+ and all anions for OH^- ions.)

Water Pollution Polluted water is water which can only support life to a limited degree (or not at all).

Cause The cause of water pollution is a lack of oxygen dissolved in the water, e.g. fertilisers from farm land and animal waste increase aquatic life, using up more oxygen. When dissolved oxygen is exhausted dead plant-life cannot decay.

Chemical waste and lead ions (from domestic pipes) also cause a large amount of water pollution.

Consequences The consequences of pollution are spread of disease, poisoned fish, etc.

Drinking Water Water treatment plants remove solids by filtration and then use chlorine to kill bacteria so that the water is safe to drink. In some areas, fluoride ions are added to domestic water to prevent tooth decay.

Properties of Water

Melting point The melting point of pure water is 0°C ⎫ at atmospheric
Boiling point The boiling point of pure water is 100°C ⎭ pressure.

51

Identification	The identification of pure water is by boiling.

Check the boiling point of an aqueous solution and, if 100°C, the water is pure.

Pure water and aqueous solutions will turn

cobalt chloride blue → pink,

anhydrous copper (II) sulphate white → blue.

Reaction with Metals

Potassium
When potassium is introduced to water there is a violent reaction. The metal melts and moves on the surface of the water, releasing hydrogen which burns with a pinkish flame. The remaining solution is alkaline.

$$2K(s) + 2H_2O(l) \rightarrow H_2(g) + 2KOH(aq)$$

Sodium
The reaction is not as violent as potassium but is similar. The metal melts and moves on the surface of the water, but the released hydrogen only occasionally catches fire.

$$2Na(s) + 2H_2O(l) \rightarrow H_2(g) + 2NaOH (aq)$$

Calcium
The reaction of calcium with water is a gentler reaction, similar chemically to that of K and Na. Since $Ca(OH)_2$ is only slightly soluble in water, a white precipitate appears.

$$Ca(s) + 2H_2O(aq) \rightarrow Ca(OH)_2(s) + H_2(g)$$

Magnesium
Magnesium reacts very slowly in cold water, faster in hot water forming magnesium hydroxide and H_2. In steam, magnesium burns to form magnesium oxide and hydrogen.

$$Mg(s) + H_2O(g) \rightarrow MgO(s) + H_2(g)$$

Zinc
Zinc reacts with steam in a similar way to magnesium.

Trend
There is a downward trend in reactions – from a vigorous reaction in cold water (K) to reaction only with steam (Zn). See Activity series (page 59).

Uses of Water
1. Water is essential for life.

2. It is a solvent.

3. Water is a raw material for many chemical processes, e.g. manufacture of ammonia and ethanol.

4. Water is used as a coolant in some power stations and other industrial processes.

2 Oxygen and Hydrogen

Occurrence of Oxygen	Oxygen is the most abundant element – occurring as compounds in most rocks.
Preparation of Oxygen	
(a) By catalytic decomposition	*Catalytic decomposition of hydrogen peroxide (H_2O_2).*
Catalyst	Manganese (IV) oxide, MnO_2
Equation	$2H_2O_2(l) \xrightarrow[\text{of } MnO_2]{\text{Catalyst}} 2H_2O(l) + O_2(g)$
Apparatus	

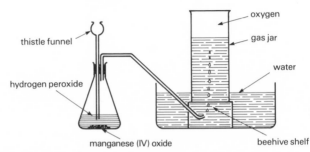

(b) By electrolysis	*Electrolysis of acidified water.* O_2 is given off at the anode (+), while hydrogen is given off at the cathode (–).
Properties	1. Oxygen is a colourless, odourless gas.
	2. Density – similar to that of air.
	3. Solubility in water – slightly soluble.
Test for Oxygen	A glowing splint (*heat, fuel*) is reignited in *oxygen* (see Fire Triangle, page 47).
Uses of Oxygen	1. Supports life (respiration) and combustion.
	2. Rocket fuel mixtures.
	3. Manufacture of steel.
	4. Welding (in oxy-acetylene torches).
	5. Medicine – oxygen-enriched air.
Oxides	Oxides are compounds made of an element and oxygen only. They are often made by heating the element in oxygen.
Examples	$2Mg(s) + O_2(g) \rightarrow 2MgO(s)$
	$S(s) \quad + O_2(g) \rightarrow SO_2(g)$

Metal Oxides   Some metal oxides like Na_2O are soluble in water, giving alkaline solutions.

Example $Na_2O(s) + H_2O(l) \rightarrow 2NaOH(aq)$

Others may be insoluble in water, like CuO, Fe_2O_3, Al_2O_3.

Non-metal Oxides   Some non-metal oxides like CO_2 and SO_2 are soluble in water, giving acidic solutions.

Example $SO_2(g) + H_2O(l) \rightarrow H_2SO_3(aq)$ (sulphurous acid)

Others may be insoluble in water, like SiO_2.

Classification of Oxides

Basic   Basic oxides are those which react with acids to form salts.

Examples $\underline{Na}_2O(s) + 2HCl(aq) \longrightarrow 2\underline{Na}Cl(aq) + H_2O(l)$

$\underline{Cu}O(s) + H_2SO_4(aq) \longrightarrow \underline{Cu}SO_4(aq) + H_2O(l)$

and MgO, K_2O, CaO, FeO, Fe_2O_3

> Note: The element occurs in the salt in the positive ion.

Acid   Acidic oxides are those which react with alkalis to form salt.

Examples $\underline{S}O_2(g) + 2NaOH(aq) \rightarrow Na_2\underline{S}O_3(aq) + H_2O(l)$

and CO_2, oxides of nitrogen.

> Note: The element occurs in the salt in the negative ion.

Amphoteric   Amphoteric oxides are those which react with acids to form salts but also react with alkalis to form different salts.

Examples $\underline{Al}_2O_3(s) + 6HNO_3(aq) \rightarrow 2\underline{Al}(NO_3)_3(aq) + 3H_2O(l)$

acting as a base

$\underline{Al}_2O_3(s) + 2NaOH(aq) \rightarrow 2Na\underline{Al}O_2(aq) + H_2O$

acting as an acid   sodium aluminate

(Aluminium hydroxide can react in a similar way.)

> Note: Another amphoteric oxide is zinc oxide.

Formation of Hydrogen (H_2)   *Reactive metals and water (or steam).*

From sodium $2Na(s) + 2H_2O(l) \rightarrow H_2(g) + 2NaOH(aq)$

water

From magnesium	$Mg(s) + H_2O(g) \rightarrow H_2(g) + MgO(s)$
	steam

Metals and dilute acids

From iron $Fe(s) + H_2SO_4(aq) \rightarrow H_2(g) + FeSO_4(aq)$

> Note: Copper does *not* release hydrogen from any acid.

Electrolysis of acidified water or brine.

From acidified water
H^+ ion is attracted to the cathode (–):

$$2H^+(aq) + 2e^- \rightarrow H_2(g)$$

Manufacture
Hydrogen is produced from natural gas, by reacting methane with steam 700°C and 30 atmospheres pressure using a catalyst of nickel:

$$CH_4(g) + H_2O(g) \rightarrow 3H_2(g) + CO(g)$$

Removal of CO
The carbon monoxide (CO) is oxidised to carbon dioxide (CO_2) and removed.

Properties of Hydrogen
Hydrogen is a colourless, odourless gas.

Density
It is very light (M_r of H_2 = 2, compared with 28 for N_2 in air).

Solubility
Hydrogen is insoluble in water.

Collection of gas
It is collected by upward delivery (also called downward displacement of air).

H_2 gas

Burning of Hydrogen
If ignited, hydrogen burns to form water.

Safety Precautions
Safe storage, no naked flames.
Avoid contamination with air.

Hydrogen as a reducing agent
Hydrogen can reduce some metal oxides to metals.

Example $CuO(s) + H_2(g) \rightarrow Cu(s) + H_2O(g)$

This only occurs with less reactive metals, such as copper, silver and gold (see Activity series, page 59).

Uses of Hydrogen
1. Manufacture of ammonia.

2. Manufacture of margarine.

    vegetable oil + hydrogen $\rightarrow$ margarine (solid)

3. Hydrogen as a fuel. The advantages are that hydrogen burns to form water only (no pollution); and, in space travel, recycling is possible. The disadvantages include difficulty of storage and the risk of explosion.

13 Periodic Table

Periodic Table The Periodic Table of Elements is an arrangement of the chemical elements in order of increasing atomic number, with elements which have similar properties placed in the same vertical column.

		METALS							NON-METALS					Gp 0

(Periodic Table diagram)

METALS ┤ $_1$H ├ NON-METALS — Gp 0

Gp I	Gp II							Gp III	Gp IV	Gp V	Gp VI	Gp VII	$_2$He
$_3$Li	$_4$Be	Period					$_5$B	$_6$C	$_7$N	$_8$O	$_9$F	$_{10}$Ne
$_{11}$Na	$_{12}$Mg						$_{13}$Al	$_{14}$Si	$_{15}$P	$_{16}$S	$_{17}$Cl	$_{18}$Ar
$_{19}$K	$_{20}$Ca				$_{26}$Fe		$_{29}$Cu	$_{30}$Zn				$_{35}$Br
		transition metals									$_{53}$I
								$_{82}$Pb			

Period A period is a horizontal row where elements with similar properties occur periodically. Each period starts with a reactive metal [sodium (Na), potassium (K), etc.] and ends with a very unreactive element, a noble gas [neon (Ne), argon (Ar), etc.].

Group A Group is a vertical column containing elements with similar properties.

Examples Group I (Li, Na, K, etc., called alkali metals)

Group II (Be, Mg, Ca, etc., called alkaline earth metals)

Group VII (F, Cl, Br, I, called halogens)

Group 0 (He, Ne, Ar, etc., called noble gases)

Group Number and Electrons The number of electrons in the outer energy level of all elements in a group is generally the same (see Group 0 below for exception).

Examples

Group I	Li	(Z = 3)	2,1
	Na	(Z = 11)	2, 8, 1
	K	(Z = 19)	2, 8, 8, 1
Group VII	F	(Z = 9)	2, 7
	Cl	(Z = 17)	2, 8, 7
Group 0	He	(Z = 2)	2
	Ne	(Z = 8)	2, 8
	Ar	(Z = 18)	2, 8, 8

In the case of the noble gases, the number in the outer energy level is the maximum for that level.

Group and Type of Element	Elements lose, gain or share electrons when forming compounds in order to get an electron structure like that of the nearest noble gas.
Group I	Group I elements lose $1e^-$ → M^+ ion.
Group II	Group II elements lose $2e^-$ → M^{2+} ion.
	Elements forming positive ions are generally *metals*.
Group VII	Group VII elements may gain $1e^-$ → X^- ion. Elements forming negative ions are generally *non-metals*.

> Look carefully at the table on page 56 and note how it divides into metals and non-metals.

Transition Metals	Transition metals are the metals in the middle section of the Periodic Table, between the vertical columns containing the elements in Group II and Group III.
Compounds	These metals generally form coloured compounds (e.g. blue copper, Cu^{2+} salts).
Valency	They have more than one valency, e.g. iron, Fe^{2+} and Fe^{3+}.
Catalysts	They are used as catalysts, e.g. vanadium (V) oxide in manufacture of sulphur trioxide, $SO_3(g)$, from sulphur dioxide, $SO_2(g)$, in the Contact process for making sulphuric acid; and manganese (IV) oxide MnO_2, in the decomposition of hydrogen peroxide in making oxygen.
Order of Reactivity	
Group I	Li in water – metal does not melt, but reacts steadily. Na in water – melts and reacts vigorously. K in water – melts and reacts violently so that H_2 gas formed catches fire. So K is more reactive than Na (reactivity increases down the group).
Why?	Group I (and II) elements react by losing electrons. The further the outer electron is from the positive nucleus, the less strongly it is held and the more easily it can be lost. So the element further down the group is the most reactive.
Group VII	The most reactive element is fluorine (F) at the top. These elements react by gaining electrons. The closer the incoming electron is to the nucleus the more strongly it will be held.

Differences in Properties between Metals and Non-metals

	Metals	Non-Metals
Physical state at 20°C	Generally solids (exception mercury).	Can be solid, liquid (bromine only), or gas.
Melting point	Generally high (sodium and potassium are quite low).	Generally low (exceptions: diamond, graphite and silicon).
Shininess	Generally shiny, mostly silvery appearance.	Solid may be shiny but rarely silvery.
Malleability	Malleable (i.e. able to be beaten into sheets).	Brittle when solid.
Ductility	Ductile (can be drawn into wire).	—
Thermal conductivity	Good conductors.	Non-conductors (insulators).
Electrical conductivity	Good electrical conductors.	Generally non-conductors (exception: graphite).
Formation of oxides	Form basic oxides (exceptions: Al_2O_3 and ZnO which are amphoteric).	Form acidic oxides.

Tests to Identify an Element as Metallic or Non-metallic

	Metallic	Non-metallic
Burn in oxygen	Oxide formed is a solid.	Oxide formed is often a gas.
Solubility of oxide	If soluble, will give an alkaline solution. If insoluble, will react with an acid to form a salt.	Non-metal oxides are mostly soluble in water to give an acid solution.
Electrical conductivity	If element conducts it is most likely to be a metal.	

14 Metals

Activity Series Metals are placed in order of their reactivity (with the most reactive at the top).

Most reactive

Potassium	(K)
Sodium	(Na)
Calcium	(Ca)
Magnesium	(Mg)
Aluminium	(Al)
Zinc	(Zn)
Iron	(Fe)
Hydrogen	(H)
Copper	(Cu)

Least reactive

The more reactive the metal, the greater is the likelihood that it will form ions. (Hydrogen is included in the series since, like metals, it forms a positive ion H^+.)

Displacement When a solid metal X is placed in a solution containing ions of a less reactive metal Y, the less reactive metal is displaced as the solid metal:

$$X(s) \quad + \quad Y^{2+}(aq) \rightarrow Y(s) + X^{2+}(aq)$$

more reactive   less reactive

Example 1 *Iron (Fe) metal in copper (Cu^{2+}) solution.*
Fe is above Cu, so Fe will finish as Fe^{2+} ions.
For this to happen copper metal will be displaced from its ions:

$$Fe(s) + Cu^{2+}(aq) \rightarrow Cu(s) + Fe^{2+}(aq)$$

Example 2 *Zinc (Zn) metal in magnesium (Mg^{2+}) solution.*
Mg is above Zn, so Mg will finish as Mg^{2+} ions. Mg^{2+} ions are already present, so no reaction needs to occur.

Example 3 *Hydrogen (H_2) gas and copper oxide (CuO).*
H is above Cu, so H will finish as a compound.
H_2 will displace Cu from Cu^{2+} (in CuO):

$$H_2(g) + CuO(s) \rightarrow Cu(s) + H_2O(l)$$

Example 4 *Magnesium (Mg) metal in dilute hydrochloric acid (HCl).*
Mg is above H, so Mg will finish as Mg^{2+} ions.
To achieve this H_2 gas will be displaced from H^+ ions (in the acid):

$$Mg(s) + 2HCl(aq) \rightarrow MgCl_2(aq) + H_2(g)$$

Example 5	*Copper (Cu) metal in dilute hydrochloric acid (HCl).* H is above Cu, so H will finish as a compound. H is already present as HCl(aq), so no reaction will occur.
Position of an Unknown Metal	The position of an unknown metal can be determined by placing the metal in a series of solutions of known metal ions (and H$^+$ ions) and seeing which metals are displaced. A check of position can be made by adding different known metals to solutions of the unknown metal ion.

Reactions with Air

Potassium Sodium Calcium Magnesium	All burn in air to form oxides.
Example	$2Mg(s) + O_2(g) \rightarrow 2MgO(s)$ (Burns with a bright flame).
Aluminium	Aluminium reacts slowly with air to form a protective aluminium oxide (Al_2O_3) coating; but when heated, burns to form the oxide.
Zinc	Zinc burns in air to form zinc oxide.
Iron	Iron rusts in the cold in the presence of moisture. Iron also burns in air to form Fe_2O_3. Note that iron (III) oxide forms since O_2 in air is an oxidising agent.
Copper	When strongly heated in air, black copper oxide (CuO) is formed.

Reactions with Water (or Steam)

In general	Metal + H_2O → metal oxide or hydroxide + $H_2(g)$
Trend	Reactions become more difficult as one moves down from potassium to copper.
Potassium	Potassium reacts violently in *cold* water → alkaline solution. (The hydrogen released catches fire). $2K(s) + H_2O(l) \rightarrow 2KOH(aq) + H_2(g)$
Sodium	Sodium reacts vigorously in *cold* water → alkaline solution. (The hydrogen released only occasionally catches fire.)
Calcium	Calcium reacts steadily in *cold* water → alkaline solution (milky due to partially dissolved calcium hydroxide) and hydrogen. $Ca(s) + 2H_2O(l) \rightarrow Ca(OH)_2(s) + H_2(g)$

Magnesium	Magnesium reacts slowly in *cold* water (equation similar to that with calcium), but reacts readily in *steam* → magnesium oxide and hydrogen.
Aluminium	Aluminium does not react if the oxide coating is left on.
	If the oxide layer is removed, aluminium reacts vigorously to form aluminium hydroxide $Al(OH)_3$ and hydrogen H_2.
Zinc	Zinc reacts with *steam* → zinc oxide $ZnO(s)$ and hydrogen H_2.
Iron	Iron reacts with steam → $Fe_3O_4(s)$ and hydrogen H_2.
Copper	Copper does *not* react with water or steam.

Reactions with Dilute Acids

In general	Metal + dilute acid → salt + hydrogen, except that dilute nitric acid behaves differently.
Trend	The trend from potassium to copper is from very reactive to unreactive.
Magnesium	Magnesium + hydrochloric acid:

$$Mg(s) + 2HCl(aq) \rightarrow MgCl_2(aq) + H_2(g)$$

Iron	Iron + sulphuric acid:

$$Fe(s) + H_2SO_4(aq) \rightarrow FeSO_4(aq) + H_2(g)$$

Note: Iron (II) sulphate is formed since dilute sulphuric acid is not an oxidising agent.

Copper	Copper does not react with dilute hydrochloric or sulphuric acids (and *never* releases hydrogen from an acid).

Storage of Alkali Metals

Potassium ⎫ Sodium ⎬ Lithium ⎭	These metals are so reactive with water that they have to be stored under oil.

Occurrences of Metal Ores

Compounds	Most metals occur in the earth's crust as compounds.
Chlorides	These include NaCl (rocksalt), $MgCl_2$ – containing the more reactive metals.
Oxides	These include Al_2O_3 (bauxite), ZnO, and Fe_2O_3 (haematite).
Free metal	A few metals (the least reactive ones) occur naturally as the element: copper, gold, silver.

61

Extraction of Metal Ores

Electrolysis   The more reactive metals need to be extracted from their ore by electrolysis. It can provide the large amounts of energy needed to force the metal ion to take back the electrons.

Examples   Na from NaCl (molten), and Al from Al_2O_3.

Reduction with carbon   The reducing agent, carbon, is used as coke to convert several metal oxides to the metal.

Examples   Fe from Fe_2O_3 in the blast furnace (see below).
Zn from ZnO, and Cu from CuO.

Environmental problems   Air pollution arises from impurities in the metal ores.
Surface pollution is mainly holes and scars from mining, together with spoil tips and slag heaps.

Recycling of Metals   The earth contains a limited supply of all metals.
Collecting, treating and re-using (i.e. re-cycling) is essential to help maintain the supply.

Iron Ore   The ore is haematite, Fe_2O_3.
Iron is the second most abundant metal. (Aluminium is the most abundant).

Extraction of Iron

Raw Materials   Haematite, coke and limestone.

Blast Furnace

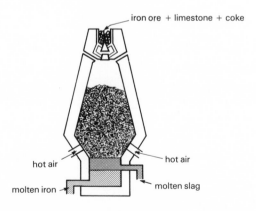

Reactions   Coke + air → carbon dioxide
$$C(s) + O_2(g) \rightarrow CO_2(g)$$

Formation of CO CO_2 is reduced by coke to CO:
$$CO_2(g) + C(s) \rightarrow 2CO(g)$$

Reduction of Fe_2O_3	$Fe_2O_3(s) + 3CO(g) \rightarrow 2Fe(l) + 3CO_2(g)$
Limestone	The limestone is decomposed by the heat to form CaO and CO_2: $CaCO_3(s) \rightarrow CaO(s) + CO_2(g)$
Slag	CaO is a basic oxide and reacts with acidic impurities (mainly SiO_2) from the ore to form a slag, which is less dense than molten iron – so floats on it.
Iron metal	The iron metal formed in the blast furnace is not very pure, the main impurity being carbon. This crude iron is called *pig iron*.
Making Steel	The pig iron from the blast furnace is not very useful, because it is very brittle. It is treated by removing some carbon and adding other elements to form steels.
The Oxygen Furnace	An oxygen furnace is used to make steels. Oxygen is blasted into the molten iron to oxidise some of the carbon to carbon dioxide (CO_2), leaving certain precise amounts of carbon. Precise amounts of other elements are added to make a steel with the required properties.

Examples   Mild steels———————————————→Hard steels
                              (percentage of carbon increases)

Stainless steel is an alloy that contains chromium.

High speed steel is an alloy that contains tungsten.

Rusting of Iron

Reaction $4Fe(s) + 3O_2(aq) \rightarrow 2Fe_2O_3(s)$
                                          rust

This will only take place in the presence of water.

Proof of conditions   Four experiments can be carried out:

1. Iron nails in tap water (containing dissolved O_2).
                                                    Nails *rust*.

2. Iron nails in ordinary air (containing water vapour).
                                                    Nails *rust*.

3. Iron nails in dry air – in sealed tube containing a drying agent (e.g. anhydrous calcium chloride). Nails *do not rust*.

4. Iron nails in boiled water (boiled to remove dissolved O_2) and with oil or wax on top of water (to prevent fresh O_2 dissolving). Nails *do not rust*.

Protection of Iron and Steel   To keep oxygen and water from the surface of the iron or steel, one can use a number of methods.

Greasing   Greasing is used for moving parts, but has to be renewed.

Painting	Painting is used for large objects (e.g. bridges), but needs to be re-applied if the surface is broken.
Galvanising	The steel is galvanised by being coated with a layer of zinc metal. If the surface is scratched, the oxygen reacts with the zinc rather than the iron. (Zinc is more reactive than iron.)
Tin-plating	Steel cans are coated with tin, but tin is less reactive than iron, so if the surface is scratched, the iron reacts.
Chromium-plating	The steel is plated (by electrolysis) with chromium. This offers some protection, but it is mainly for decoration.
Sacrificial metals	On the hull of a ship, bars of a metal, such as zinc or magnesium, are attached. These metals are more reactive than iron and so react, and are 'sacrificed'.

Properties of Iron
Iron is a typical metal – but is magnetic.

Iron reacts with non-metals.

Examples $Fe(s) + S(s) \rightarrow FeS(s)$

$2Fe(s) + 3Cl_2(g) \rightarrow 2FeCl_3$

Iron also reacts with acids.

Example   *Dilute sulphuric acid.*

$Fe(s) + H_2SO_4(aq) \rightarrow FeSO_4(aq) + H_2(g)$

Aluminium

Abundance	Aluminium (Al) is the most abundant metal in the earth's crust (7.5% of all elements).
Occurrence	It occurs in most rocks and clays.
	It is obtained commercially from bauxite (Al_2O_3).
Extraction	Pure aluminium is obtained by electrolysis as described in Chapter 7.

Properties of Aluminium

Physical	Typical metal – but low density (2.7 g/cm^3). (Compare: iron 7.9 g/cm^3 and copper 8.9 g/cm^3.)
Chemical	Oxide coating protects metal, so it is not very reactive unless the coating is removed.
	Al will react with acids and alkalis to release hydrogen.
$Al_2O_3/Al(OH)_3$	Both show amphoteric behaviour (see page 54).

Anodising of Aluminium	If a piece of aluminium is made the anode of an electrolytic cell in which oxygen gas is released, an additional oxide coating is obtained. If a dye is added to the electrolyte, the colour is absorbed and a coloured aluminium object can be made.
Thermite Process	Aluminium can displace metals below it in the activity series. If mixed with Fe_2O_3 and ignited, molten iron can be formed in the highly exothermic (generating heat) process.

Uses of Metals

	Use	Reason
Magnesium	Alarm flares, flash bulbs	Reactive metal
Aluminium	Domestic: Kitchen foil, pans, window frames. Industrial: Car engines, power cables, aeroplanes.	Light and strong
Zinc	Galvanising steel	More reactive than iron
Iron	Construction, transport	Strong metal
Copper	Electrical wiring Water pipes	Good conductor of electricity Low reactivity

Alloys	Alloys are specific mixtures of metals and other elements.
Examples	Bronze is a mixture of copper and tin.
	Solder is made of tin and lead (and other mixtures).
	Steel is made up of iron and other elements.
Use of Alloys	An alloy is usually designed for a particular purpose, making use of the properties of the individual components.
Example	Titanium is used in alloys for hip-joints and rockets, due to its low density and high melting point.

15 Salt to Chlorine

Salt	Salt is sodium chloride. It is found in sea water and rock salt.
Purification of Rock Salt	Purification is achieved by the following means:

1. Dissolving the salt (NaCl) in hot water.
2. Filtering to remove undissolved impurities and give filtrate of NaCl solution.
3. Evaporation of sufficient water from filtrate to give a saturated solution.
4. Crystallisation of NaCl when saturated solution cools.
5. Filtration of NaCl crystals.
6. Drying of crystals.

Structure of NaCl

Bonding Ionic:

$$Na \text{ atom} \quad \text{donates 1e}^- \text{ to} \quad Cl \text{ atom}$$
$$2,8,1 \qquad\qquad\qquad\qquad 2,8,7$$
$$\downarrow \qquad\qquad\qquad\qquad\qquad \downarrow$$
$$Na^+ \text{ ion} \qquad\qquad\qquad Cl^- \text{ ion}$$
$$2,8 \qquad\qquad\qquad\qquad 2,8,8$$

Oppositely charged ions are attracted to form Na^+Cl^-.

Na^+Cl^- crystals Salt crystals have Na^+ and Cl^- ions arranged in a lattice with opposite ions next to each other, as shown in the diagram in Chapter 4.

Uses of Salt

Health Salt is essential for maintaining body metabolism. Too much salt may lead to high blood pressure. Too little salt may lead to high heat exhaustion.

De-icing Roads Salt is added to roads so that a solution of salt is formed, which freezes at a temperature lower than 0°C, *but* salt on roads speeds up the rate of rusting of cars.

Sodium Hydroxide Sodium hydroxide (NaOH) is also known as *caustic soda* (caustic = burning), and is obtained in industry from salt.

Reactions of Sodium Hydroxide

With Acids Acid + NaOH(aq) → Na^+ salt + H_2O

With ammonium salts	Ammonium salt + NaOH(aq) → NH_3(g) + H_2O + Na$^+$ salt
Example	$(NH_4)_2 SO_4$(aq) + 2NaOH(aq) → 2NH_3(g) + 2H_2O(l) + Na_2SO_4(aq)
With Metal ions	In many cases they form insoluble hydroxides which can be used to identify the metal.
Example	Ca^{2+}(aq) + 2OH$^-$(aq) → $Ca(OH)_2$(s) white cloudiness

Other Precipitates

$Mg(OH)_2$(s)	white
$Zn(OH)_2$(s) (amphoteric)	white, but soluble in extra NaOH
$Al(OH)_3$(s) (amphoteric)	white, but soluble in extra NaOH
$Fe(OH)_2$(s)	green
$Fe(OH)_3$(s)	red-brown
$Cu(OH)_2$(s)	pale blue

Uses of sodium hydroxide

1. Removal of grease, e.g. in oven cleaners.

2. Manufacture of soaps (by reacting with fats).

3. Manufacture of paper.

Sodium Hydrogen Carbonate

Sodium hydrogen carbonate ($NaHCO_3$) is also known as *sodium bicarbonate*.

Example of reaction with acid

Sodium hydrogen carbonate + hydrochloric acid

→ sodium chloride + carbon dioxide + water

$NaHCO_3$(s) + HCl(aq) → NaCl(aq) + CO_2(g) + H_2O(l)

Uses of sodium hydrogen carbonate

1. Baking – used to release CO_2 to make cakes, etc., rise. Often mixed with tartaric acid, as baking powder.

2. Antacid – used as remedy for indigestion.

Chlorine

Chlorine (Cl_2) is a greenish gas, denser than air, fairly soluble in water. It is a choking, toxic, oxidising agent and a bleaching agent (e.g. moist litmus turned to white).

Uses of Chlorine

1. In making bleach.

> Note: Never mix bleach with other domestic cleaning agents.

2. Water treatment – chlorine is added to mains water at treatment plants to kill bacteria so it is safe to drink.

3. Manufacture of other products, such as PVC and chlorinated solvents.

4. Making pesticides – but some cause long-term pollution.

Chlorine in the Periodic Table

Chlorine occurs in Group VII (Halogens):

$$\left.\begin{array}{l}\text{Fluorine}\\\text{Chlorine}\\\text{Bromine}\\\text{Iodine}\end{array}\right\}$$ Outer energy level of each halogen contains $7e^-$. Each tries to gain (or share) $1\,e^-$ when forming compounds.

Properties

Fluorine – yellowish gas | density and | reactivity↑
Chlorine – greenish gas | boiling point | increases
Bromine – reddish liquid | increase
Iodine – silvery solid ▼

Displacement

A more reactive halogen displaces a less reactive halogen from its ions:

Cl_2 displaces Br_2 (or I_2) from a solution containing Br^- (or I^-),

Br_2 displaces I_2 from a solution containing I^-,

but I_2 will not displace Cl_2 or Br_2

> Note: The more reactive halogen always finishes as its ion if it can.

Example

$Cl_2(g) + 2I^-(aq) \rightarrow I_2(aq) + 2Cl^-(aq)$

Chlorine and Iron

Dry chlorine passed over heated iron wool reacts to form iron (III) chloride.

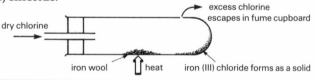

dry chlorine → | excess chlorine escapes in fume cupboard
iron wool ⬆ heat | iron (III) chloride forms as a solid

> Note: Iron (III) chloride is formed because chlorine is an oxidising agent.

Test for Halides

Halide in solution, plus dilute nitric acid and silver nitrate solution.

If the precipitate is white then a chloride is present;
          creamish then a bromide is present;
          pale yellow then an iodide is present.

In each case the insoluble silver halide is formed.

Example

$Br^-(aq) + AgNO_3(aq) \rightarrow AgBr(s) + NO_3^-(aq)$

16 Limestone and Carbon Dioxide

Limestone

Occurrence Limestone occurs naturally as calcium carbonate ($CaCO_3$) in limestone rocks, also in chalk and marble.

Extraction It is extracted by quarrying, though this leaves holes and scars on the surface of the earth.

Hard Water

rain water (initially pure)	+	dissolved carbon dioxide from air	+	limestone

hard water

Equation

$$H_2O(l) + CO_2(g) + CaCO_3(s) \rightarrow Ca(HCO_3)_2(aq)$$

calcium hydrogencarbonate

Calcium hydrogencarbonate is soluble in water, so the resulting solution contains Ca^{2+} ions and is classified as 'hard'.

> Note: Mg^{2+} ions from magnesium rocks also cause hardness.

Reactions of Calcium Carbonate

Thermal decomposition

$$CaCO_3(s) \xrightarrow[\text{heat}]{\text{strong}} CaO(s) + CO_2(g)$$

limestone — quicklime

Lime kiln The lime kiln is the tower in which, in industry, limestone is mixed with coke and heated. The quicklime (CaO) is removed at the bottom.

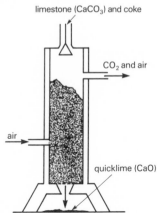

limestone ($CaCO_3$) and coke

CO_2 and air

air

quicklime (CaO)

Addition of acids Calcium carbonate reacts with acids with effervescence (fizzing) of CO_2.

Example $CaCO_3(s) + 2H^+(aq) \rightarrow Ca^{2+}(aq) + CO_2(g) + H_2O(l)$

Uses of Calcium Compounds	Common calcium compounds are:
	calcium carbonate ($CaCO_3$), calcium oxide or quicklime (CaO), and calcium hydroxide or slaked lime [$Ca(OH)_2$].
Agriculture	All three are used to control soil acidity.
Cement	Clay and gypsum ($CaSO_4$) as well as limestone are required in the manufacture of cement.
Blast furnace	Limestone enables acid impurities to be removed as slag.
Glass	Glass is made by melting together limestone, sand and sodium carbonate.

Carbon Dioxide	
Preparation	Marble chips are reacted with dilute hydrochloric acid in apparatus similar to that used for the preparation of hydrogen.
Equation	$CaCO_3(s) + 2HCl(aq) \rightarrow CaCl_2(aq) + CO_2(g) + H_2O(l)$
Burning of fossil fuels	When fossil fuels are burned *completely* (i.e. in plenty of air) carbon dioxide is produced.
Example	$CH_4(g) + 2O_2(g) \rightarrow CO_2(g) + 2H_2O(g)$ methane

> Remember: When burned in insufficient air, carbon monoxide (CO) is formed.

Properties of Carbon Dioxide	
Physical	1. Colourless, odourless gas.
	2. Fairly easily solidified $\rightarrow$ 'dry ice'.
	3. Density – heavier than air ($M_r = 44$).
	4. Slightly soluble in water $\rightarrow$ weakly acidic solution.
Chemical	1. *Magnesium.* Magnesium ribbon continues to burn in carbon dioxide. $2Mg(s) + CO_2(g) \rightarrow 2MgO(s) + C(s)$

> Note: Mg is oxidised by CO_2; CO_2 is reduced.

2. *Carbon*.
In the blast furnace, carbon dioxide is reduced by coke.

$$CO_2(g) + C(s) \rightarrow 2CO(g)$$

3. *Alkalis*.
Carbon dioxide reacts with alkalis to form salts.

Test for Carbon Dioxide

1. Carbon dioxide bubbled into lime-water → cloudy solution.

$$CO_2(g) + Ca(OH)_2(aq) \rightarrow \underset{\text{insoluble}}{CaCO_3(s)} + H_2O(l)$$

2. More carbon dioxide bubbled into cloudy solution
→ clear solution.

$$CaCO_3(s) + CO_2(g) + H_2O(l) \rightarrow \underset{\text{soluble}}{Ca(HCO_3)_2(aq)}$$

> Note: Reaction 2 is the same as that for the formation of hard water.

Test for Metal Carbonates

On heating, metal carbonates generally decompose to give carbon dioxide which can be identified using lime-water.

Uses of Carbon Dioxide

Fire extinguishers

An atmosphere of carbon dioxide will not allow fuels to burn, due to the exclusion of oxygen (see Fire Triangle).

Fire extinguishers involving carbon dioxide can be of two main types.

Type A: *Compressed carbon dioxide* in a cylinder.

Type B: *Acid/Carbonate*. Some extinguishers contain a small bottle of acid above a solution of sodium hydrogen carbonate ($NaHCO_3$). When activated the acid reacts with the sodium hydrogen carbonate to form carbon dioxide and a water solution, which is sprayed on the fire.

> Note: Type B must *not* be used on electrical fires.

Carbonated Drinks

These include beer, lemonade, soda water, etc.

Carbon Cycle

In the earth's atmosphere, the ratio of oxygen (O_2) : carbon dioxide (CO_2) stays approximately constant. The biochemical changes involving each substance, both in air and on earth, balance one another. This is known as the carbon cycle.

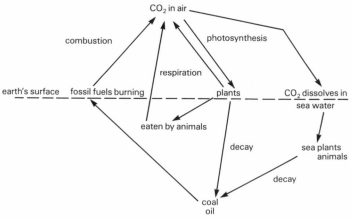

Photosynthesis $\dfrac{\text{Carbon}}{\text{dioxide}}$ + water $\xrightarrow[\text{chlorophyll}]{\text{sunlight}}$ glucose + oxygen

Respiration   Glucose + oxygen $\longrightarrow$ $\dfrac{\text{carbon}}{\text{dioxide}}$ + water + $\dfrac{\text{energy}}{\text{released}}$

The Greenhouse Effect   The balance of the carbon cycle has been upset by the burning of fossil fuels, increasing the proportion of carbon dioxide in air; and by the destruction of forests, reducing the take-up of carbon dioxide by photosynthesis. The increase in carbon dioxide in the atmosphere is thought to allow more infra-red radiation from the sun to be absorbed, so less heat escapes, and the surface temperature of the earth increases.

7 Rates of Reaction

Rate in terms of Product	Rate in terms of product is the rate at which a product is formed.

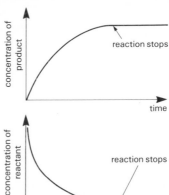

Rate in terms of Reactant	Rate in terms of reactant is the rate at which a reactant is used up.

Steepness of curve The steeper the curve the faster the reaction (i.e. the higher the rate). As the curve becomes more shallow (i.e. less steep), the reaction slows down.

Factors Affecting Rate

(a) Concentration of Reactant The more reactant there is present, the faster the rate. Look at the second graph. When the concentration of reactant is higher, the curve is steeper. When the concentration is lower, the curve is more shallow.

Why? When the concentration is higher, there are more reactant molecules around, and so the chance of molecules colliding (and reacting) is greater.

Example $Mg(s) + 2HCl(aq) \rightarrow MgCl_2(aq) + H_2(g)$

The higher the concentration of HCl (in mol/l), the higher the rate.

Gas pressure The pressure of a gas is equivalent to the concentration of a solution. The more gas particles, the higher the pressure. So an increase in gas pressure will increase the rate of reaction.

(b) Particle Size The smaller the size of solid reactant particles, the faster the reaction.

Example Large lumps of marble with HCl produce a slower reaction, whereas powdered marble with HCl produces a faster reaction:

$$CaCO_3(s) + 2HCl(aq) \rightarrow CO_2(g) + H_2O(g) + CaCl_2(aq).$$

73

Why?   For the same mass of reactant, there is a much greater surface area with small pieces than with one large lump. Compare the surface area of 1 cube 10 mm each side (= 600 mm^2) with 1000 cubes each 1 mm side (= 6000 mm^2): they both occupy the same total volume, 1000 mm^3. The greater the surface area, the more molecules that will be exposed to the acid.

(c)
Temperature   The higher the temperature, the faster the reaction.

Example   If hot hydrochloric acid of the same concentration is used in the reaction with magnesium above, the metal will be completely reacted much more quickly than with acid at room temperature.

Why?   The higher the temperature, the more kinetic energy the molecules possess; and so the reactants will collide with greater force and with a greater chance of a reaction occurring.

(d)
Catalyst   A catalyst is a chemical which speeds up a chemical reaction, but which is chemically unchanged at the end.

Example   Decomposition of hydrogen peroxide using manganese (IV) oxide as catalyst, in the preparation of oxygen (Chapter 12):

$$2H_2O_2(aq) \xrightarrow{\text{MnO}_2} 2H_2O(l) + O_2(g).$$

With the catalyst absent, hydrogen peroxide decomposes only slowly (a few gas bubbles) at room temperature, but if the catalyst is added a rapid effervescence occurs. The more catalyst that is present, the faster the reaction.

Enzymes   Enzymes are natural catalysts.

(e)
Light   The rate of certain reactions is increased by the presence of light.

Example 1   *Silver halides, such as silver chloride (AgCl) and silver bromide (AgBr).*
Silver chloride precipitate is white when first formed, for instance in reaction of salt solution with silver nitrate solution, NaCl(aq) with AgNO$_3$(aq); but turns grey/purple on standing in light. If the white precipitate is protected from light, it stays white. This is important in photography where the unexposed film contains silver halides.

Example 2   *Photosynthesis* takes place in daylight.

Changes in
Graphs   Consider the reaction of calcium carbonate with hydrochloric acid, CaCO$_3$(s) with HCl(aq).

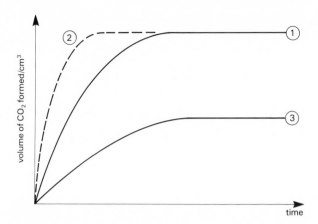

Graph 1   Standard.

Graph 2   Same volume of CO_2 formed but more quickly, due to:

      (a) higher concentration of HCl, or

      (b) higher concentration of $CaCO_3$, or

      (c) smaller particles of $CaCO_3$, or

      (d) higher temperature, or

      (e) catalyst present.

Graph 3   Half the volume of CO_2 formed, due to half the mass of $CaCO_3$ taken [assuming HCl(aq) to be in excess].

18 Sulphur and Nitrogen

Sulphur

Occurrence in nature

Sulphur occurs naturally as the element in 'sulphur beds', in volcanic regions. It sometimes occurs as sulphide ores: for instance, copper sulphide (CuS) and iron (II) sulphide (FeS). Sulphur also occurs in crude oil, natural gas and coal. (The sulphur needs to be removed during refining to prevent pollution later.)

Properties of Sulphur

Physical

1. Non-metallic element, yellow solid at room temperature.
2. Melting point fairly low (melts to brown liquid).
3. The solid is brittle; can be powdered.
4. Non-conducting.
5. Insoluble in water.

Chemical

1. Combustion – readily burns in air with blue flame:

   $S(s) + O_2(g) \rightarrow SO_2(g)$.

2. Iron and sulphur:

   $Fe(s) + S(s) \rightarrow FeS(s)$ (see page 6).

Uses of Sulphur

1. Making sulphuric acid (see below).
2. Hardening of rubber (vulcanisation).

Properties of Sulphur Dioxide

Solubility

Sulphur dioxide is very soluble in water forming an acidic solution:

$SO_2(g) + H_2O(l) \rightarrow H_2SO_3(aq)$ sulphurous acid

Acid Rain

Sulphur dioxide, released into the air as a pollutant, dissolves in water vapour, and is oxidised to form sulphuric acid. This is a component of acid rain.

Smell

Sulphur dioxide has a choking smell and is an irritant poison.

Uses of Sulphur Dioxide

1. Sulphur dioxide is used as a sterilising agent and food preservative.
2. It is also a bleaching agent.

Sulphuric Acid

Sulphuric acid (H_2SO_4) is used extensively in many processes in the chemical industry.

Manufacture of Sulphuric Acid

Raw materials Sulphur, air and water.

Site of plant The plant should be near a port, for transport convenience. It should also be near a good road system.
The plant must be near a centre of population for labour, but sited so prevailing winds blow any polluted air away from town.

Process 1. $S(s) + O_2(g) \rightarrow SO_2(g)$

2. $2SO_2(g) + O_2(g) \rightleftharpoons 2SO_3(g)$ sulphur trioxide

> Note: Reaction 2 is reversible, meaning that SO_2 and O_2 are converted to SO_3 (left to right), but also SO_3 decomposes to form SO_2 and O_2 (right to left). This means, in practice, that not all the SO_2 is converted to SO_3. In industry, one chooses the conditions that will result in as much SO_3 being formed as is feasible.

Pressure used – atmospheric.
*Temperature used – about 450°C.
*Catalyst used – vanadium (V) oxide.

*These increase the rate of the reaction.

Harmful or irritant

3. The SO_3 gas formed is passed into concentrated sulphuric acid to form *oleum* (fuming sulphuric acid) which can be transported and later diluted.

Reactions of Concentrated Sulphuric Acid

Water A very exothermic (generating lots of heat) reaction occurs.

> Note: Always add acid to water.

Dehydrating agent	Concentrated sulphuric acid will chemically remove the water from certain chemicals.

Example 1   *Copper sulphate crystals.*

$$CuSO_4.5H_2O(s) \xrightarrow[H_2SO_4]{conc} CuSO_4(s) + 5H_2O(l)$$

blue crystals
(hydrated $CuSO_4$)   white crystals
(anhydrous $CuSO_4$)

Example 2   *Sugar.*

$$C_{12}H_{22}O_{11}(s) \xrightarrow[H_2SO_4]{conc} 12C(s) + 11H_2O(l)$$

black mass
remaining

Oxidising agent	Concentrated sulphuric acid will oxidise many chemicals and itself will be reduced to $SO_2(g)$.

Example   *Copper metal.*

$$Cu(s) + 2H_2SO_4(l) \rightarrow CuSO_4(aq) + SO_2(g) + 2H_2O(l)$$

Corrosive Nature   Due to its high reactivity, sulphuric acid is very corrosive. *Care needs to be taken in handling, transportation and storage.*

Corrosive

Reactions of Dilute Sulphuric Acid

Litmus H_2SO_4 turns blue litmus $\rightarrow$ red.

Metals   Most metals (but not copper) react with dilute sulphuric acid to form salt plus hydrogen.

Example   *Iron.*

$$Fe(s) + H_2SO_4(aq) \rightarrow FeSO_4(aq) + H_2(g)$$
iron (II) sulphate

Alkalis   Alkalis react with dilute sulphuric acid to form a salt and water.

Example $H_2SO_4(aq) + 2NaOH(aq) \rightarrow Na_2SO_4(aq) + 2H_2O(l)$.

Insoluble bases   Insoluble bases react with dilute sulphuric acid to form a salt and water.

Example $H_2SO_4(aq) + CuO(s) \rightarrow CuSO_4(aq) + H_2O(l)$

Metal carbonates	Metal carbonates react with dilute sulphuric acid to form a salt plus carbon dioxide plus water.
Example	$H_2SO_4(aq) + K_2CO_3(aq) \rightarrow K_2SO_4(aq) + CO_2(g) + H_2O(l)$

Uses of Sulphuric Acid

1. To make fertilisers.
2. To make detergents.
3. As battery acid (contains 30% H_2SO_4).

Test for Sulphate Ion

Solution of possible sulphate + dil HCl + $BaCl_2$ solution
$\rightarrow$ a white precipitate if $SO_4{}^{2-}$ ion is present.

Ionic equation $\quad Ba^{2+}(aq) + SO_4{}^{2-}(aq) \rightarrow BaSO_4(s)$

Nitrogen

Nitrogen (N_2) is a fairly unreactive gas, making up about 78% of air, by volume.

Uses of nitrogen

1. Nitrogen is used in the manufacture of ammonia (see below).
2. Its inertness means it can safely be used to flush out oil tanks and pipe lines. It is used in tungsten filament light bulbs, and in the storage of apples.
3. Liquid nitrogen is utilised in preserving foods by freeze drying.

Nitrogen Cycle

The nitrogen cycle is a diagram showing how nitrogen (as the element and as compounds) is conserved in nature.

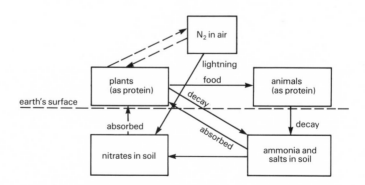

Protein

Protein is needed by animals for growth, so they eat plants, and animal waste returns nitrogen compounds to the soil.

Natural balance

The natural balance of nitrogen is no longer viable due to ever-increasing world population needing more and more food. Nitrogen compounds have to be added artificially to the soil – as fertilisers (see below).

Manufacture of Ammonia	Ammonia (NH_3) is manufactured by the Haber Process.

Raw materials

$$N_2(g) \quad + \quad 3H_2(g) \rightleftharpoons 2NH_3(g)$$

from air
by fractional
distillation of
liquid air

from methane
by its reaction with steam,

i.e. $CH_4(g) + H_2O(g) \rightarrow 3H_2(g) + CO(g)$

and

$CO(g) + H_2O(g) \rightarrow H_2(g) + CO_2(g)$

Conditions

1. Nitrogen and hydrogen gas mixed in the mole ratio 1:3.
2. Pressure – high.
3. Temperature – about 450°C.
4. Catalyst – mainly iron and aluminium oxide.

Recycling of N_2 and H_2

Since the reaction is reversible (compare manufacture of SO_3), the gaseous mixture formed contains N_2, H_2 and NH_3. When ammonia has been removed, the remaining N_2 and H_2 (still in ratio 1:3) is recycled.

Properties of Ammonia

Physical

1. Colourless gas with a characteristic pungent smell.
2. Density – less than air (M_r = 17).
3. Very soluble in water (Fountain experiment).
4. Easily liquefied.

Chemical properties

1. Ammonia turns red litmus blue.
2. Ammonia is a base. It accepts a proton from an acid.
3. Alkali – since it is a base soluble in water,

    $NH_3(g) + H_2O(l) \rightleftharpoons NH_4OH(aq)$,

    (ionises partially into NH_4^+ and OH^- ions).
4. Forms ammonium salts.
5. Can be oxidised to nitric acid (see below).

Uses of ammonia

1. Ammonia is used in the manufacture of fertilisers and itself is used as a direct fertiliser.
2. It is used in making nitric acid (HNO_3), which is essential for making many explosives.
3. Household ammonia solution is used for degreasing.

Manufacture of Nitric Acid

Oxidation of ammonia

Ammonia + air $\xrightarrow[\text{at 900°C}]{\text{catalyst}}$ nitrogen monoxide (NO)

Oxidation of nitrogen monoxide

Nitrogen monoxide + air + water → nitric acid

Reactions

Nitric acid reacts like other acids, with

metal carbonates   ⟶   salt + CO_2 + H_2O

alkalis   ⟶   salt + H_2O

insoluble bases   ⟶   salt + H_2O

Uses

Nitric acid is used in making fertilisers.
It is also used for making explosives.

Heat on Metal Nitrates

Alkali metal nitrates

Alkali metal nitrates decompose on heating to form the metal nitrite and oxygen.

Example

$2NaNO_3(s) \rightarrow 2NaNO_2(s) + O_2(g)$

Most other metal nitrates

Most other metal nitrates decompose on heating to form the metal oxide, nitrogen (IV) oxide (NO_2) and oxygen.

Example

$2Pb(NO_3)_2(s) \rightarrow 2PbO(s) + 4NO_2(g) + O_2(g)$

Fertilisers

Fertilisers are used to supplement natural sources of nitrogen, phosphorus and potassium.

Examples

N-nitrogen: ammonium sulphate, $(NH_4)_2SO_4$

              ammonium nitrate, NH_4NO_3

P-phosphorus: calcium phosphate, $Ca_3(PO_4)_2$

K-potassium: potassium chloride, KCl.

Plants need these elements for healthy growth, but different plants need different amounts of each. Leafy plants (lettuce, for instance) need a high proportion of nitrogen.

Fertilisers are sold with different NPK values written on the sack to indicate the proportions of the three elements.

Water Pollution

Fertilisers, being washed into streams and rivers cause aquatic plant life to flourish too much – and this results in water pollution.

19 Carbon

Occurrence   Carbon occurs as the element in the ground as coal, diamond, graphite; and in compounds such as carbon dioxide, carbonates, sugars and petroleum.

Allotropes   Allotropes are forms of the element in the solid state but with different structures: carbon, for instance, existing as both diamond and graphite.

Chemical Properties

Combustion   Incomplete: $2C(s) + O_2(g) \rightarrow 2CO(g)$

Complete: $C(s) + O_2(g) \rightarrow CO_2(g)$

Reducing Agent Fe_2O_3 in blast furnace: $Fe_2O_3(s) + 3CO(g) \rightarrow 2Fe(l) + 3CO_2(g)$

Copper oxide: $CuO(s) + C(s) \rightarrow Cu(s) + CO(g)$

Fossil Fuels   Fossil fuels are those derived from dead plants etc. and subsequently extracted from under the earth or sea. They are:

    coal (mostly carbon)

    natural gas (mostly methane, CH_4)

    petroleum (mostly hydrocarbons).

Combustion   All fossil fuels burn:

$$\xrightarrow{\text{in plenty of air}} CO_2(g) + H_2O(g) + \textit{heat energy}$$

$$\xrightarrow[\text{of air}]{\text{in limited supply}} CO(g) + H_2O(g) + \textit{heat energy}$$

toxic, so ventilation needed

Toxic

Efficiency   Efficiency varies from one fuel to another but depends on the amount of air available for burning. Sulphur and nitrogen compounds must be removed from fuels before they are burned.

Safety   *Flammability*.
Liquid and gaseous fuels are all flammable.

Storage.
Such fuels should be stored in a special cabinet or in a room with plenty of ventilation.

Labelling
Bottles should be labelled with a 'flammable liquid' sign.

Flammable

Flashpoint
The flashpoint of a flammable liquid is the temperature at which a liquid gives off sufficient flammable vapour to flash when a light is applied.

Coal

Origin   Coal deposits result from the decay, over millions of years, of trees and plant life, which are buried and compressed. Most other elements are removed.

Mining   Open-cast mining leaves scars on the surface.
Deep mines may cause land subsidence, and spoil heaps.
In both cases, land restoration is needed when a mine is closed.

Smokeless fuels   Smokeless fuels are sold to reduce the problem of smog.

Uses of coal   The present-day use of coal is mostly in power stations.

Petroleum and Natural Gas

Origin   The formation of petroleum and natural gas is similar to that of coal but with marine animals and plants being decayed. Gas occurs above the oil.

Location   Gulf States, Nigeria, Venezuela, USSR, North Sea and other places.

Separation   Separation is by fractional distillation in a refinery into components based on their differing boiling points. The components are mostly hydrocarbons (compounds containing carbon and hydrogen only). The larger the number of carbon atoms, the higher the boiling point.

Fractions

> A version of the table overleaf may be given to you in a Data Book.

Name of fraction	No. of C atoms per molecule	Boiling range	Use(s)
gas	1 – 4	below 25°C	domestic gas (CH_4); bottled gas (C_3H_8, C_4H_{10}); lighter fuel (C_4H_{10})
petrol	4 – 12	40° – 100°C	making petrol itself after further treatment
naphtha	7 – 14	90° – 150°C	making medicines, plastics, fibres, etc.
kerosene	9 – 16	150° – 240°C	making aviation fuel
diesel oil	15 – 25	220° – 250°C	making diesel fuel
lubricat-ing oil	20 – 70	250° – 350°C	lubrication of moving parts
bitumen	over 70	above 350°C	waterproofing roofs; roads

Further treatment   All the fractions are composed of mixtures of hydrocarbons, most of which either need to be separated further, or treated to make them more useful. The higher fractions may be refined by 'cracking' to make smaller hydrocarbons (2, 3 or 4 carbons).

Hydrocarbons   Hydrocarbons all contain the elements carbon and hydrogen only.

Bonding   Bonding is covalent (electron-sharing) between atoms. Carbon has the special property of being able to bond to other carbon atoms, i.e. to form chains. Each carbon atom needs to share 4 pairs of e^- (valency of 4) while hydrogen atoms share 1 pair of e^- (valency of 1).

Saturated hydrocarbons   Saturated hydrocarbons are those in which each carbon atom is bonded to a total of four other atoms (either carbon or hydrogen).

Example   *Alkanes*.

Unsaturated hydrocarbons   Unsaturated hydrocarbons are those in which each carbon atom is bonded to *less than* four other atoms. It can do this by sharing two or three pairs of electrons with another carbon atom.

Example   Ethene C_2H_4.

or

Where 2 pairs of electrons are shared, a double covalent bond ($C=C$) is formed. Where 3 pairs of electrons are shared a triple covalent bond ($C\equiv C$) is formed.

Alkanes   Alkanes are a group of saturated hydrocarbons which have a general formula of C_nH_{2n+2} (where n = the number of carbon atoms). The group all have similar chemical properties and their physical properties change gradualy as the number of carbon atoms increases. A group such as the alkanes is called a *homologous series*.

Methane to Propane

Methane CH_4

$$H-\underset{\displaystyle H}{\overset{\displaystyle H}{C}}-H$$

Ethane C_2H_6

$$H-\underset{\displaystyle H}{\overset{\displaystyle H}{C}}-\underset{\displaystyle H}{\overset{\displaystyle H}{C}}-H$$

Propane C_3H_8

$$H-\underset{\displaystyle H}{\overset{\displaystyle H}{C}}-\underset{\displaystyle H}{\overset{\displaystyle H}{C}}-\underset{\displaystyle H}{\overset{\displaystyle H}{C}}-H$$

Butane C_4H_{10} can be written as

$$H-\underset{\displaystyle H}{\overset{\displaystyle H}{C}}-\underset{\displaystyle H}{\overset{\displaystyle H}{C}}-\underset{\displaystyle H}{\overset{\displaystyle H}{C}}-\underset{\displaystyle H}{\overset{\displaystyle H}{C}}-H$$

Isomerism   Isomerism occurs where a molecular formula (e.g. C_4H_{10}) can be written as more than one structural formula, i.e. the atoms are joined together in a different way.

Example C_4H_{10} can be written as butane above

but also as

$$H-\underset{\displaystyle H}{\overset{\displaystyle H}{C}}-\underset{\displaystyle \underset{\displaystyle H}{\overset{\displaystyle \mid}{\underset{\displaystyle H}{\overset{\displaystyle \mid}{C}-H}}}}{\overset{\displaystyle H}{C}}-\underset{\displaystyle H}{\overset{\displaystyle H}{C}}-H$$

2-methylpropane

Butane and 2-methylpropane are referred to as *isomers*.

85

Reactions of Alkanes

Examples of combustion

$$C_3H_8(g) + 5O_2(g) \rightarrow 3CO_2(g) + 4H_2O(g)$$

Bromine

Alkanes left in sunlight with bromine slowly undergo a substitution reaction (a hydrogen bonded to a carbon is substituted by a bromine atom).

Example

$$\begin{array}{ccc}
\text{H} & & \text{H} \\
| & & | \\
\text{H} - \text{C} - \text{H} + Br_2(l) & \rightarrow & \text{H} - \text{C} - Br + HBr(g) \\
| & & | \\
\text{H} & & \text{H}
\end{array}$$

bromomethane

Alkenes

Alkenes form a homologous series of hydrocarbons with one double bond (C=C) per molecule.

Examples

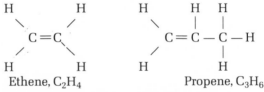

Ethene, C_2H_4 Propene, C_3H_6

Alkenes are *unsaturated* with a double bond.

Addition

Addition is possible. The double bond breaks, leaving a spare bond (or electron) on each of the two carbon atoms. New atoms can share one of their electrons to form a new bond.

The X_2 has *added* across the double bond.

Reactions of Alkenes

Bromine with water

If ethene gas is bubbled into bromine water, the red-brown colour disappears showing that the bromine has reacted.

1,2-dibromoethane

> Note: This reaction can be used as a test to distinguish between alkanes and alkenes.

Polymerisation   Alkenes can add to themselves to form a long chain called a polymer. This is done in industry using special conditions.

Example $CH_2 = CH_2 + CH_2 = CH_2 \rightarrow -CH_2 - CH_2 - CH_2 - CH_2 -$
ethene   written as $+CH_2 - CH_2+_n$
           polyethene (or polythene)

and $n\,CH_2 = CHCl \longrightarrow +CH_2 - CHCl+_n$
chloroethene   polychloroethene
(or vinyl chloride)   (or polyvinyl chloride, PVC)

In general, polymers form when small molecules (called *monomers*) join together into massive chains.
(*mono* = one, *poly* = many)

Steam   In industry, ethene is reacted with steam to form ethanol:

$$CH_2 = CH_2 + \quad H_2O \quad \rightarrow \quad \begin{array}{cc} CH_2 - CH_2 \\ | \quad\quad | \\ H \quad\quad OH \end{array}$$
$$(H-OH)$$
$$(C_2H_5OH)\ \text{ethanol}$$

Margarine   Liquid vegetable oils which are unsaturated are hardened by reacting with hydrogen in the presence of a catalyst:

$$\text{vegetable oil} + H_2 \xrightarrow[\text{addition}]{\text{partial}} \begin{array}{c} \text{hardened oil} \\ \text{(margarine)} \end{array}$$

Manufacture of Ethene   Ethene is manufactured by 'cracking' of petroleum fractions.

Ethanol   Ethanol is the chemical name for what is commonly known as 'alcohol'.

Fermentation   Sugar solution is mixed with yeast and left at 25°C for several days:

$$\text{sugar} \xrightarrow[\text{in the warm}]{\text{enzymes in yeast}} \text{ethanol} + CO_2(g)$$

The carbon dioxide can be shown to be released by testing the gas evolved with limewater, which will turn cloudy (or milky). The solution formed after fermentation is distilled to give almost pure ethanol.

Products   The products of fermentation include beers, wines and spirits. Care should be taken with alcoholic drinks due to their short-term effect and possible serious long-term effect on the body.

Oxidation of ethanol	Ethanol in wines is oxidised by air to ethanoic acid (the major component of vinegar):

$$C_2H_5OH \xrightarrow{\text{oxidation}} CH_3COOH$$
$$\text{ethanoic acid}$$

This reaction explains the 'souring' of wines exposed to air.

Uses of ethanol	1. Ethanol is used in meths as a solvent. Meths (methylated spirits) is ethanol to which a poison (methanol) and a dye are added to stop people drinking it.
	2. Ethanol is used as a fuel in alcohol burners.
Ethanoic Acid	Ethanoic acid (CH_3COOH) is a typical weak acid.
	It forms salts like hydrochloric acid, nitric acid, etc.
Soaps	Soaps are salts of an acid, such as stearic acid (similar to ethanoic acid, but with a longer chain of carbon atoms) formed by boiling animal fats with sodium hydroxide:

animal fats + NaOH → soaps
(containing compounds   (such as sodium
related to stearic acid)   stearate)

Plastics	Plastics are polymers which can soften on heating and harden on cooling.
Thermo-softening plastics	These can be softened by heating and cooled *many times*.
Examples	Polythene, PVC, polystyrene, nylon.
Thermosetting plastics	These can be softened by heating and cooled *once only*.
Examples	Melamine, bakelite.
Formation	The principal raw material is petroleum:

$$n \text{ (monomer)} \longrightarrow \text{polymer}$$

Danger	Many plastics burn very readily, giving off toxic fumes.
Environmental hazards	Most plastics do not decay naturally (i.e. they are not biodegradable). When they are discarded, they become pollutants and a waste of our natural resources.

Energy and Chemical Change

Energy Changes In most chemical reactions, energy is either *given out* from the surroundings (e.g. tube gets hotter) or *taken in* from the surroundings (e.g. tube gets colder).

Heat is the most usual form of energy associated with chemical reactions, but light and electrical energy are also met.

Exothermic Exothermic reactions are those where *heat is given out* (Ex = out, as in exit).

Endothermic Endothermic reactions are those where *heat is taken in*.

Units of heat change The units of heat change are joules or kilojoules per mole of a specified chemical.

Symbol The symbol for heat change is ΔH.

For *exothermic* reactions, ΔH is *negative*, i.e. heat is given out, so products have less stored energy than the reactants.

For *endothermic* reactions, ΔH is *positive*, i.e. heat is absorbed, so products have more stored energy than the reactants.

Exothermic Changes

Example 1 *Combustion* (a) $C(s) + O_2(g) \rightarrow CO_2(g)$ $\Delta H = -394$ kJ/mol

(b) $CH_4(g) + 2O_2(g) \rightarrow CO_2(g) + 2H_2O(g)$

$\Delta H = -882$ kJ/mol

(c) *Respiration*
Sugar $+ O_2 \rightarrow CO_2 + H_2O +$ energy

Example 2 Water added to anhydrous $CuSO_4$. ΔH negative

Example 3 Conc. H_2SO_4 added to water. ΔH negative

Example 4 *Neutralisation reactions*. For instance:

$HCl(aq) + NaOH(aq) \rightarrow NaCl(aq) + H_2O(l)$ $\Delta H = -57$ kJ/mol

Endothermic Changes

Example 1 *Photosynthesis.*

$CO_2 + H_2O +$ energy $\rightarrow$ sugar $+ O_2$

Example 2 *Dissolution of certain salts.* For instance:

$KNO_3(s) \rightarrow KNO_3(aq)$ $\Delta H = +35$ kJ/mol

Example 3 *Electrolysis reactions* (see overleaf).

Measurement of Heat Changes Temperature readings can be taken over a period of time to find the rise (or loss) in temperature.

Example In a neutralisation reaction a known volume of alkali is measured into an insulated beaker and a stop-clock started. Temperature readings are taken at half-minute intervals. At a certain time (possibly 3 minutes), a known volume of acid is added to the beaker and temperature readings are taken for a further 5 or 7 minutes.

A graph of temperature against time will give the rise in temperature (ΔT) on neutralisation.

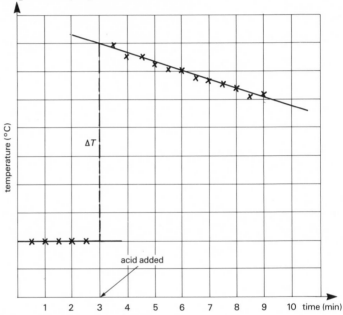

Calculations from Equations How many kJ of heat will be released when 11 g of propane is burned completely in air?

Given: $C_3H_8(g) + 5O_2(g) \rightarrow 3CO_2(g) + 4H_2O(g)$ $\Delta H = -2200$ kJ/mol

From equation 1 mol C_3H_8, on burning completely, releases 2200 kJ

∴ 44 g $C_3H_8(M_r = 44)$ releases 2200 kJ

∴ 11 g C_3H_8 releases $2200 \times \dfrac{11}{44}$

= 550 kJ

Energy Involved in Starting a Reaction Do exothermic reactions always start spontaneously?

No. When methane is mixed with air it does not burn until a flame is applied.

Energy has to be supplied to start off the reaction. Once started, it can continue on its own. This energy is called the *activation energy*.

Reversible Reactions	The same amount of energy is released in a reaction going in one direction as is absorbed in going in the other direction.
Examples	$CuSO_4.5H_2O(s) \rightarrow CuSO_4(s) + 5H_2O(l)$ $\Delta H = +x$ kJ/mol
	$CuSO_4(s) + 5H_2O(l) \rightarrow CuSO_4.5H_2O(s)$ $\Delta H = -x$ kJ/mol
Bond-breaking/-forming	Generally, when bonds are broken, heat needs to be put in (endothermic); but when bonds are formed, heat is released (exothermic).
Other forms of Energy	Most of the examples above concern changes in heat energy.
Light energy	Light energy is involved in photosynthesis and in photographic film.
Electrical energy	Electrical energy is another form of energy often met in chemical reactions.
Electrolysis	Electrolysis involves the breakdown of chemicals by electrical energy. *All electrolysis processes are endothermic.*
Chemical Energy	Chemical energy is involved when any chemical change occurs. The energy changes may be:

chemical energy → heat energy   (exothermic)

heat energy   → chemical energy (endothermic)

light energy   → chemical energy (endothermic)

electrical energy → chemical energy (endothermic)

chemical energy → electrical energy (exothermic)

Chemical Cells In a chemical cell a chemical reaction is used to make electrical energy. If the apparatus below is set up, electrons flow from the zinc rod, through the external wire, to the copper rod, giving a voltmeter reading, i.e. an electric current flows.

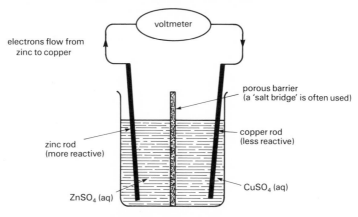

91

Half-equation	at zinc rod: $\quad$ $Zn(s) - 2e^- \rightarrow Zn^{2+}(aq)$
	at copper rod: $\quad$ $Cu^{2+}(aq) + 2e^- \rightarrow Cu(s)$

Ionic equation	$Zn(s) + Cu^{2+}(aq) \rightarrow Zn^{2+}(aq) + Cu(s)$
Other pairs of metals	Other pairs of metals will give similar results, but with different voltmeter readings.
	The more reactive metal will dissolve while the less reactive metal will be deposited.
Activity Series	Activity series can be determined using the above technique and comparing metals in pairs.
Applications of chemical cells	1. Dry cell batteries are used in radios, clocks, etc.
	2. Lead-acid accumulators are used in car batteries.
	3. Fuel cells are used in space vehicles.

Energy Resources

These are of two types.

Non-renewable	Renewable
fossil fuels	hydro-electric power
nuclear fuels	solar power
	wind power
	tidal power
	geothermal power

Choice of energy source	The choice of energy source depends on economic considerations (e.g. cost of tidal barrages, solar cells) and environmental considerations (e.g. pollution from fossil fuels, possible nuclear radiation).

Nuclear Power

Origin	Unstable nuclei break down spontaneously, releasing energy (as well as alpha, beta and gamma radiation).
	The energy released can be harnessed to provide electricity.
Costs	Nuclear power stations are very expensive to build but cheap to run.
Dangers	Great care has to be taken in maintaining the plant, and in handling the radioactive source materials as well as disposing of radioactive waste.
Half-life	The half-life of a radioactive isotope is the time taken for half of the original material to decay. Half-life varies for different isotopes, from seconds to millions of years.

21 Tests for Common Substances and Ions

This chapter contains a summary of the tests for different substances and ions which appear elsewhere in the text in the appropriate topic chapters.

> Note: Care should always be taken when carrying out tests where gases might be evolved. Only attempt to smell gases when under the supervision of a teacher.

Tests for Common Substances

Hydrogen

Hydrogen gas is colourless, odourless (no smell) and lighter than air. It has no effect on moist red or blue litmus paper.

To test for the gas a lighted splint is carefully held near the mouth of the inverted tube. If hydrogen is present, the gas will either burn quietly or explode ('pop') and condensation may be seen on the inside of the tube.

Oxygen

Oxygen is colourless and odourless, and has no effect on moist red or blue litmus paper.

To test the gas, a glowing splint is placed in the tube. It bursts into flame if the gas is fairly pure oxygen.

Carbon dioxide

Carbon dioxide is colourless and odourless, and turns moist blue litmus paper to red. It is heavier than air.

When bubbled through lime-water it turns cloudy (or milky).

If more carbon dioxide is bubbled through the solution, it turns clear.

Sulphur dioxide

Sulphur dioxide is a colourless gas with a choking smell (CARE). It is very soluble in water and heavier than air.

The gas will turn moist blue litmus paper red and a piece of filter paper soaked in potassium dichromate solution will turn from orange to green.

Ammonia

Ammonia is a colourless gas with a characteristic pungent smell (CARE). It is very soluble in water and lighter than air.

The gas will turn moist red litmus paper to blue.

Chlorine

Chlorine has a slight greenish colour and a choking smell (CARE). It is slightly soluble in water and heavier than air.

It will turn moist blue litmus paper to red and then quickly bleach it.

When bubbled into a solution of potassium iodide, a yellow-brown colouration appears.

Water   Water, when pure, boils at 100°C.

Water solutions turn anhydrous copper sulphate powder from white to blue, and cobalt chloride crystals from blue to pink.

Tests for Ions Present in Compounds   The tests for each of the following ions may give conclusive evidence for its presence or it may only give a strong indication.

(a) Cation Tests

> Remember: Cations are positive ions which, in electrolysis, are attracted to the cathode (–).

Ammonium ion   All ammonium salts will give off ammonia gas when sodium hydroxide solution is added. It is often necessary to warm the solution gently to detect the gas.

Addition of NaOH(aq)   Several cation solutions will form a precipitate when sodium hydroxide solution is added. It is important to add it slowly and, if a precipitate (ppt.) forms, to add excess sodium hydroxide to see if the precipitate dissolves.

Ion	Precipitate
calcium	white, often slow in forming
magnesium	white
aluminium	white, which dissolves in excess sodium hydroxide
zinc	white, which dissolves in excess sodium hydroxide
iron (II)	green, which turns yellowish on walls of tube, on standing
iron (III)	red-brown
copper (II)	pale-blue

Flame tests   Metals in Groups I and II of the Periodic Table often give a colour to a non-luminous bunsen flame when their salts are put into the flame. The salt is applied either as a solid or as a solution on a clean flame test wire. Two examples are given below.

Sodium ion   Persistent bright orange – yellow flame (like the common street light) appears.

Potassium ion   A pinky (lilac) colour appears in a small part of the flame, which can only be seen for a few seconds.

(b) Anion Tests

> Remember: Anions are negative ions which, in electrolysis, are attracted to the anode (+).

If trying to identify an unknown anion, it is important to perform these tests in the order given. Otherwise, erroneous results may be obtained.

Nitrate ion

If an ammonium ion has been found in the cation test, it is important to boil the sample with sodium hydroxide until no more ammonia is released. After cooling, add aluminium powder (or Devarda's alloy) and some more sodium hydroxide solution, and warm gently. (CARE: hydrogen gas is formed.) If a nitrate ion is present, ammonia gas will be detected.

Carbonate ion
Hydrogen-carbonate ion

Addition of dilute hydrochloric acid to the sample will give effervescence of carbon dioxide.

Sulphate ion

The sample is dissolved in deionised (or distilled) water. Dilute hydrochloric acid is added, followed by barium chloride solution. A white precipitate is formed if a sulphate ion is present.

Halide ion

(That is: a chloride, bromide or iodide ion.)

The sample is dissolved in deionised water and dilute nitric acid is added. When silver nitrate solution is added, a curdy precipitate may be formed as follows:

chloride ion – a white ppt. which turns greyish or purple on exposure to light. The ppt. dissolves in aqueous ammonia.

bromide ion – a creamy-coloured ppt.

iodide ion – a pale yellow ppt.

Index

Acid rain 49, 76
Acids 37 – 39
Activation energy 90
Activity series 59
Air 9, 48
Air pollution 49
Alkali metals, storage 61
Alkalis 37
Alkanes, alkenes 85 – 87
Allotropes of carbon 82
Alloys 65
Aluminium 64
Aluminium ion, test for 94
Aluminium oxide, electrolysis 33
Ammonia 80
Ammonia, test for 93
Ammonium ion, test for 94
Anion tests 95
Anode 33
Atom 15
Atomic number 16
Atomic structure 16
Bauxite 33
Blast Furnace 46, 62
Boiling 10
Boiling Point 7
Bonding 18
Brine, electrolysis 34
Bromide ion, test for 95
Calcium ion, test for 94
Calcium, reaction with water 52
Carbon 82
Carbon cycle 71
Carbon dioxide 70
Carbon dioxide, test for 93
Carbon monoxide 49
Carbonate ion, test for 95
Catalyst 74
Cathode 33
Cation tests 94
Caustic soda 66
Cells, chemical 91
Centrifugation 7
Chemical symbol 15
Chloride ion, test for 95
Chorine 67
Chlorine gas, use in water purification 51
Chlorine, test for 93
Chromatography 8
Chromium-plating 64
Combustion 47
Composition of matter 13
Compounds 5
Compressibility of gases 14
Concentration of solutions 30
Condensation 10
Conductors 32
Copper solutions, electrolysis 35
Copper (II) ion, test for 94
Copper, refining 35
Covalent bonding 20
Cracking 84
Cryolite 33
Diamond 22
Diffusion 13
Displacement of metals 59
Dissolution 7
Distillation 7
Ductility 58
Electric current 32
Electrical conductivity 23
Electrochemistry and electrolysis 32
Electron 16
Electron arrangement 18
Electroplating 36
Elements 5, 15
Empirical formula 28
Endothermic changes 89
Energy changes 89
Energy levels 18

Energy resources 92
Enzymes 74
Equation, ionic 38
Equations 25
Ethanoic acid 88
Ethanol 87
Evaporation 8, 10
Exothermic changes 89
Fertilisers 81
Fermentation 87
Filtration 7
Fire triangle 47
Flame tests 94
Flashpoint 83
Fluoride ions in tap water 51
Formulae, from mass composition 28
Formulae, writing of 24, 25
Fossil fuels 49, 70, 83
Fractional distillation of liquid air 48
Freezing 10
Fuels, combustion 49
Galvanising of steel 64
Giant molecular solids 22
Graphite 22
Greenhouse effect 72
Haber process 80
Haematite 62
Half-life 92
Halide ions, test for 68, 95
Halogens 68
Hard water 50, 69
Hazard signs 17, 46, 77, 78, 82, 83
Hydrocarbons, saturated and
  unsaturated 84
Hydrochloric acid(aq), electrolysis 36
Hydrogen 20, 54
Hydrogen chloride, bonding 20
Hydrogen peroxide, in preparation of
  oxygen 53
Hydrogen, test for 93
Hydroxides of metals 40, 67
Indicators 38
Iodide ion, test for 95
Ion exchange 51
Ionic bonding 19
Ionic solids, structure 23
Ions 15, 19, 24
Iron and steel, protection 63
Iron (II) and iron (III) ions, tests for 94
Iron, extraction 62
Isomerism 85
Isotopes 16, 92
Kinetic energy 13
Kinetic particle theory 13
Lead compounds, as air pollutants 49
Limestone 69
Macromolecular solids 22
Magnesium chloride, bonding 20
Magnesium ion, test for 94
Magnesium, reaction with water 52
Malleability 58
Manganese (IV) oxide, as catalyst 53
Mass number 16
Melting point 23
Metal extraction 62
Metal nitrates, effect of heat 81
Metal ores 61
Metals, bonding 21
Metals 59 – 65
Metals/non-metals, properties 58
Methane 21, 85
Mixtures 5
Molar volume 28
Mole 25
Molecules 15
Natural gas 83
Neutralisation 38
Neutron 16
Nitrate ion, test for 95
Nitric acid, manufacture 81

Nitrogen 9, 79
Noble gases 18
Non-conductors 32
Nuclear power 92
Nucleus, nuclides 16
Order of reactivity in Groups 57
Oxidation 44
Oxides of nitrogen, as air pollutants 49
Oxides, classification 54
Oxidising and reducing agents 46
Oxygen 9, 53
Oxygen furnace 63
Oxygen, bonding 20
Oxygen, test for 93
Paraffin wax 22
Perchloroethene 11
Periodic table 56
Petroleum 83
pH scale 37
Photosynthesis 72
Plastics 88
Poly(ethene) 22, 87
Polymerisation 87
Potassium ion, test for 94
Potassium, reaction with water 52
Pressure 14
Proton 16
PVC 87
Radioactivity 16
Rate of reaction 73
Reactants and products 25
Reduction 44
Relative masses 17
Respiration 48, 72
Reversible reactions 91
Sacrificial metals 64
Salts 41
Sand 22
Saturated solution 11
Sea of electrons 21
Separation 5
Slag from blast furnace 63
Soaps 88
Sodium chloride 66
Sodium chloride, electrolysis 33, 34
Sodium chloride, bonding 19
Sodium hydrogencarbonate 67
Sodium hydroxide 66
Sodium ion, test for 94
Sodium, reaction with water 52
Solubility 11
Solubility in water 23
Spectator ions 38
States of matter 5
Steels 63
Sublimation 9
Sulphate ion, test for 95
Sulphur 6, 76
Sulphur dioxide 76
Sulphur dioxide, test for 93
Sulphur dioxide, as air pollutant 49
Sulphuric acid 77
Sulphuric acid, electrolysis 34
Temperature 14
Thermite process 65
Tin-plating of steel 64
Titration, procedure 39
Titration results, calculations from 30
Transition metals 57
Valency 25
Vegetable oils, hardening 87
Volume 14
Water 22, 50
Water of crystallisation 17
Water (acidified), electrolysis 34
Water, test for 94
Zinc ion, test for 94